Wear Comfortable Shoes

Surviving and Thriving as a Caregiver

Peter W. Rosenberger

Dedicated to:

Frank and Joyce Wentzky
Lloyd Mayer, posthumously
Diane Copeland
Richard and Kim Rosenberger

These individuals understand caregiving in ways few do.
I am grateful for their influence, love, experience, and wisdom.

The Delta Doctrine

While flying Delta Airlines to Atlanta one day, I discovered that flight attendants state the best advice for caregivers – all day long:

"In the unlikely event of the loss of cabin pressure, oxygen masks will drop from the ceiling. Securely place your mask on first, before helping anyone next to you who may need assistance."

That small directive, what I call "The Delta Doctrine," contains applicable wisdom for so many life circumstances – but probably none as poignant as for those of us serving as a caregiver for a chronically ill/disabled loved one.

Compassion and love often mistakenly lead us to hold our own breath – while trying to help someone else breath, but once we make that decision, it is only a matter of time before we find ourselves gasping for air. If we are unable to breathe, how can we help anyone else?

Yet, many of Americas' 65 million caregivers desperately try to assist a vulnerable loved one – while growing dangerously close to "blacking out" themselves. Grabbing the mask first is not a sign of selfishness, but rather the whisper of wisdom. Unfortunately, that soft voice is hard to hear over the often-deafening cries of someone we love.

Those who "push the wheelchair" serve as the critical team player for a suffering patient. Sadly, few know how to create a sustainable care structure for themselves. Simply getting sleep and eating a good diet is not enough. Caregivers must remain health physically, financially, emotionally, professionally, and spiritually – but that is impossible to do without reaching for the mask first.

Help is available, but a caregiver must be willing to accept that help – while tuning out the fear (and sometimes panic) that can consume us during high stressful moments. On a plane, one must simply reach for the mask that dangles. For caregivers, however, reaching for help looks quite different. Most of the conflicts with caregiving involve some sort of relationship dynamics. If the patient is bleeding or injured, then it is a medical crisis and that involves a different set of skills and needs – generally referred to as triage.

Caregiving scenarios that strain the bonds of friends, family, and marriage could benefit from "emotional triage." Since the one who suffers will, by definition, probably not be providing leadership in those areas, it is up to caregivers to ensure their own safety and well-being. Just as paramedics train to care for an agitated (and sometimes even violent) patient, caregivers can learn a few tips to protect their own emotional safety and peace of mind.

When the "turbulence of caregiving" hits, three simple things I do immediately help calm me down so that I can make healthy and positive decisions in high-stress moments: Wait, Water, Walk.

Wait Take a moment before responding. Regardless if the culprit is dementia, drugs, or just your loved one being a jerk, all types of "emotional tug-of-wars" seem to be happening simultaneously while caregiving. If you pick up the rope and involve yourself in a tug-of-war, one of two things will happen: You will win and end up on your rear – or you will lose and end up on your face.

Don't pick up the rope! Simply wait before responding. Rarely do you have to apologize or make amends for something you didn't say. Breathe slowly (inhale four seconds – exhale eight seconds), until you feel yourself growing calmer. Stress and anger are toxic for good decisions.

Water Drink some cool water. It will buy you time to think a littler clearer. Avoid sugary drinks or even coffee, and instead grab a bottle or glass of water. Your body needs water – your brain needs water. From high blood pressure to fatigue, water helps a myriad of issues. A tanked up brain functions better. Drink to think!

Walk Caregiving creates extreme stress, so when things are bouncing off the walls, take a few moments to put on some comfortable shoes and walk off some of that tension. By doing so, you are truly putting on the mask first, getting better oxygen to your body and brain, and bleeding off anxiety. Walking immediately helps facilitate calmness. Settling yourself down allows you to bring your "A-Game" to the caregiving scenario.

Wait, Water, Walk cost little or nothing – but can instantly help a caregiver make better decisions, calm down, and feel more at peace. That is the initial step of the *Delta Doctrine*. "Put your mask on first" is the most responsible and caring step in your efforts to help others. In doing so, the patient gets a healthier, confident, stronger, and more "self-controlled" caregiver - who can provide leadership while offering love.

While putting on the mask, it is important to remember that caregiving is a marathon not a sprint—wear comfortable shoes.

Acknowledgments

In writing this book, a great debt is owed to a few key individuals:

My Parents - Dr. and Mrs. Beryl Rosenberger I can't say more to you than I normally say in our millions of phone calls. You continue to speak such wisdom and encouragement into my life, and I am deeply grateful for such loving and wise parents.

Jim and Carol Parker - for extraordinary "grand-parenting."

Liz Griffith You are a wonderful sister and a great friend. Thanks for pushing me, challenging me, and loving me.

Parker and Viveka Rosenberger When I see your faces, my heart overflows with joy. Parker, even as a child, you worked to help relieve some of your mother's challenges. With pride and deep emotions, I watched your great heart develop as you journeyed into your mother's suffering. You're an awesome man, and I am so proud to be your father.

Grayson Rosenberger You and I understand each other and have a deep mutual respect. I can't think of a more wonderful thing for a father and son to share. As with your brother, your back has born its share of burdens. But you both are stronger and better men because of the difficulties you've endured. Whether on a snowy trail in Montana, or seeing you in uniform at *West Point*, you strengthen and encourage me more than I can express.

Gracie Your suffering is beyond my understanding. Although I cannot comprehend God's purpose in allowing you to endure so much, I am grateful that you modeled trusting Him with brutal realities. Because your faith is strong, mine is strengthened. Thank you for every song you've ever sung to me. I love you!

caregiver (kɛəgɪvə) — n Also called: carer a person who has accepted responsibility for looking after a vulnerable neighbor or relative.

- *Collins English Dictionary*

Introduction

Spring 1989, Nashville Tennessee
St. Thomas Hospital, 5th floor 3:00AM

The bitter taste of another cup of old coffee filled my mouth as I hunched over a stack of medical records. Caffeine and stress fought against me as I tried in vain to steady my shaking hands while scanning seemingly endless reports. The smell of fresh vomit staining my clothes still filled my nostrils and contributed to the tears filling my eyes. Ignoring the looks of nurses and staff, I sat half way down the dimly lit ward with my back against the wall and scanned over charts, lab reports, and doctors' notes in the massive folder that bore the name of my wife. In spite of three years of marriage, that night served as my first opportunity to review the file that had steadily grown since her car accident at age seventeen on November 18, 1983.

After that wreck and a long recovery, Gracie returned to Nashville's Belmont University where I first met her. Mutual friends felt us a perfect match, and, from the first moment I saw her, I agreed.

"Peter, she's wonderful, but you need to know that she had a serious car accident that left her permanently hurt," one of Gracie's friends warned.

Several others, including her family, repeated the admonition as our relationship grew, but with no frame of reference as to what the caution meant - I plunged ahead.

Nodding my head with an understanding I lacked, I assumed that no matter what her injuries, I still wanted to meet her. Obviously still alive and resuming some sort of life, I thought, "How bad could the car wreck have been - if she's back at school and others were trying to set us up?"

As she walked down the sidewalk, I swear to you that the sun followed her every step. Although noticing the limp, it didn't detract. This girl was beautiful in ways that I could not express. A nearby friend offered a squeegee to help with the drool flowing from my open mouth as I watched her head my way. Surprising me with her forthrightness, she walked right up to me, stuck out her hand and, with a voice that still causes angels to cock their heads in order to hear her better, smiled and said, "Hi Peter, I'm Gracie Parker. I need to sit down. May I put my feet in your lap?"

Plopping her misshapen feet into my lap, we sat with a group of friends in the courtyard by the student center. Noticing the scars extending above the ankles and disappearing under her cropped jeans, I "smoothly" blurted out, "Good Lord girl, what happened to you?!"

With a direct look, her frank but understated remark was only, "I had a bad car accident."

A whirlwind courtship and three years of marriage later, I sat outside a hospital room in the middle of the night, covered in Gracie's vomit following her enduring a *gran mal* seizure. This time, I directed the same question to the pile of medical documents in front of me.

*"Good Lord girl, what **happened** to you?"*

Not even her family had read what I now studied. Pouring through doctors' notes, I realized Gracie's accident was unlike anything I imagined. This was no fender-bender resulting in a broken limb that would simply serve as a weather indicator for life. Turning the pages, one word just kept flooding my mind: *devastation*.

Tears hit a few of the pages, as I hung my head in grief and hopelessness. For the first time in my life, I felt a despair that would hover over me for the next dozen years.

Reading until dawn, I closed the massive folder and sadly noted that the cover stated, "Volume 4 of 4." Before converting most of her records electronically years ago, the volumes grew to seven.

The events of that night forever altered me, along with the way I view life, hospitals, doctors, other people, my wife, and even God. Although immature, a sincere desire to care for an extraordinary woman led me into this journey. I never imagined, however, that the road would contain such suffering, loss, heartache, self-sacrifice, failure, and love.

I felt trapped.

My love for her committed me to an existence dominated by constant brutal realities—that would end with a funeral, but hopefully not mine. The avoidance of my death is not for the reasons one might think. My death would remove me from the daily burden of caring, but create an even greater hardship for my family. So even "driving off a bridge" represented a poor option.

A difficult place for a twenty-five-year-old man.

A difficult place for a fifty-one-year-old man.

Gracie's book, *Gracie-Standing With Hope* (©2010 Liberty University Press), recounts the events of the night of that seizure. I will not revisit them now, other than to communicate the changes sparked in me as it relates to serving as a caregiver, and the choice I made—and the choices I continue to make.

To date, Gracie's journey has led her through more than seventy operations, multiple amputations (not just both legs, but multiple revisions on both legs), treatment by nearly sixty physicians in a dozen hospitals, and soaring medical costs now cresting $9 million.

As her sole caregiver for nearly three decades, I often recall that lonely night spent reading her chart for the first time. Somehow, however, I pushed the massive despair into an emotional box somewhere. My choice made, I threw myself into the task of fixing that which cannot be fixed, and managing that which cannot be managed.

My wife, my responsibility: end of discussion. Besides, no one else volunteered for the job.

Decades later, I still wake up daily with the responsibility of caring for another human being; one who lives with a severe disability and suffers from intractable pain. Some days my duties involve housework, cooking, and other household tasks. Other days find me working with insurance companies or confronting physicians and providing leadership to her medical team. Sometimes I do all at the same time, while managing a company, and being a father. Armed only with a relentless persistence, a well-developed sense of humor, a few "smarts," and a degree in music (composition, *piano principal*), I somehow keep the plates spinning.

In all modesty, when it comes to want-to-be standup comedians who majored in music while serving as a caregiver —I am the best.

After countless explanations of benefits (EOB) from now six different insurance companies covering a massive amount of procedures and medical needs, I have never lost an appeal. From nurses to surgeons, I have confronted, managed, appealed to, and recruited more medical professionals to my viewpoint than I can number. Providing them the respect earned by their training, I treat each of them with deference, but not subservience. As I shared with one surgeon recently, "With all due respect, Doctor, I've cared for Gracie since you were in junior high school - and I know what I'm talking about."

Each medical professional who cares for my wife receives a paycheck; I do not. Volunteering does not make me special, but I am different. My stake in the journey is unlike those who do it for a living. My status as a spouse also places me in a category distinct from relatives who volunteer. I remain the only person in Gracie's life not connected by blood or money who has willingly chosen to care for her in this manner.

Recognizing that fact is helpful, since it provides insights into motivations, which in turn provides an opportunity to explore the needs others and I have, and "what keeps us at the table." For example, I do not appeal to doctors based upon their "love" of my wife. They may have respect kindness, affection, and even love (to a point) for her - but ultimately "love" is not the motivating force with any of the professionals treating her.

Sadly, rather than love, guilt and obligation often motivate family members (including spouses). Knowing why someone does something, can help identify the core needs of that individual, which can be important when dealing with a caregiver.

Another part of caregiving involves dealing with the inner workings of the health care system. I learned years ago that negotiating with insurance companies is not complicated, but can be challenging. Insurance companies are in business to make money for the corporation if they are for-profit, or to provide a mechanism to provide a service while also maintaining financial integrity - if they function as a not-for-profit.

Decades of dealing with insurance companies impressed upon me a great awareness, "they are not bad, they are not good - they just are." Although countless employees from insurance companies have said "no" to me, I ignore their decision and press on if it involves something that Gracie's doctor states that she requires. Over the last several decades, a half-dozen insurance companies learned that I do not take "no" for an answer, and I will be unrelenting in my pursuit. They also learned that I know my subject matter, can speak intelligently on the topic, will be courteous, and that my opinion, more often than not, is correct.

Ego does not drive that conviction, history and understanding does.

My list of accomplishments in navigating America's health care system is impressive and substantial, but not the purpose of this book. Yes, I achieved on a level few would or could, but those are external successes borne out of a fear of failure, survival instincts, and an often misguided desire to earn approval. The successes only illustrate a competency to speak to the various issues daily faced by caregivers.

The passion, however, is not to equip an army of medical negotiators. Rather than providing a course on insurance, my experience teaches me that caregivers cry out for *assurance*.

Someone once asked me, "If possible, what would you say to your younger self?"

That question and I spend a lot of time together. So many things flood my mind of what to tell the younger version of myself. Practical and encouraging alike, I would love to share assurance, tips, and wisdom to ease his journey a bit. As a young man, I did not know how to properly care for myself.

Caregiving spills into every area of the caregiver's life and each area needs addressing. Rest and a good diet are only the beginning. Not only was I unaware of how to care for myself properly, but also oblivious of how to ask for help in a way that others (or myself) could understand.

Among other things, this book serves as a "Gestalt-Type" plan of care for the twenty-five-year-old frightened husband and father who hunched over his wife's medical chart.

With the simple goals of equipping caregivers with the language skills to ask for help, as well as encouragement to accept such help, I also hope to inspire non-caregivers to better recognize and attend to the caregivers they know.

Understanding and accepting that many of the challenges faced by caregivers only resolve through the death of a loved one, my goal is to equip and empower those caregivers to focus on life. Joy, peace, and even happiness await each caregiver, regardless of the circumstances.

I cannot reach my younger self, so I'm going to do what I can. Serving as a caregiver "...since the Cold War," I've had ample time to make virtually every mistake possible, and I use that experience to equip others to bring their "A-Game" to the brutal challenges of caregiving. Dealing with my wife's massive medical issues has taught me a few things about the America's healthcare system. Living with a chronic crisis and being married to someone with extreme pain and disability - has taught me a few things about perseverance, love, and relationships.

After a particularly brutal stretch, I recall once sitting with a counselor and trying to put the pieces together. Listening for a while, the counselor told me, "I'd offer you a book to read ...but you're the guy to write it." With those words in mind, I did write the book - and I wrote it to the 23-year-old version of myself who took the helm of a catastrophic health care crisis armed with nothing but love, a few smarts, and wacky sense of humor.

Recognizing that most caregivers abruptly start their journey with little or no training - or warning, I seek to offer "just in time" tips learned over a lifetime of caregiving. With practical help my passion is to strengthen my fellow caregivers - one weary heart at a time.

Coming along side others, I offer wisdom acquired about love, life, and caregiving in my journey of watching over someone with a broken body for more than a quarter of a century.

Peter W. Rosenberger
Nashville, TN

Table of Contents

Caregiver

Greater love hath no man than this,
that a man lay down his life for his friends.
John 15:13 King James Version

The vast caregiving community is filled with people from all walks of life. From a wife looking at her husband of forty years secretly wondering how much longer he will remember her name, to the weary mother caring for her child who suffers from a debilitating disease. Pain shoots up and down a father's spine because he's spent years lifting his daughter who cannot walk due to cerebral palsy and severe cognitive impairment. A teenager grows angry when his classmates make fun of his mother who "looks different."

While I check on my beautiful wife each time I see her sleeping to make sure she's still breathing because she takes massive doses of pain killers to curb the agony of her broken body, a short drive away a weary woman watches her widowed mother step further into old age while simultaneously caring for her husband who just had a major surgery and permanent life changes.

A son looking with sorrow at his once strong father who now fights to do even the simplest of tasks, while parents of a son with hemophilia who just want him to have a normal life, spend the better part of each day worried about bruising, emergency room visits, and the threat of HIV from transfusions.

With her small children struggling to understand, a young mother watches her husband die a horrible death from a ravaging disease. A single mother raises a child with a disability alone because her husband bailed on the marriage and family.

Every day, I encounter individuals struggling with scenarios just like these. I've looked into pain-filled eyes of people who want to care for their loved ones but find themselves so blinded by frustration and weariness, that they sometimes resent the ones they love so dearly; even to the point of secretly praying that death would end this ordeal.

Sometimes it is thrust upon instantly due to trauma or the birth of a child with special needs. Other times, old age or Alzheimer's slowly and cruelly pull our loved one away from us in increments. Regardless, the challenges of caregiving can be brutal, and have broken the heart, spirit, and even body of many individuals.

We've all heard the phrase, "caring for the caregiver," but what does that really look like on a day to day basis?

How is that fleshed out while dealing with the constant crises that dominate every day?

What does that look like to my younger self as I read the horrific report of my wife's injuries; injuries that happened three years before we even met?

By opening this book, you are taking a deeper step into honestly evaluating and facing the swirling feelings brought on by the challenges you face as a caregiver for a vulnerable loved one. It is good to address those feelings, but let's be honest; "emoting" doesn't help you very much in the marathon that is your life as a caregiver.

Serving as a caregiver remains the hardest task I've ever accepted. With so many conflicting emotions, finding mental peace and quiet often seems impossible. Torn between a deep love for my spouse and the thorny feelings associated with constant caring for the needs of another human being , I often close my eyes and think of a happy place; usually one with a hammock and no one else around. Sometimes, however, I still see myself back in that hospital, hunched over Gracie's chart with eyes filling with tears.

Mistakes? Oh, I've made so many it would take a team of experts to unravel them - and to deal with those mistakes I often feel I've been raised by a "pack of therapists."

Yet, even those missteps can serve as valuable lessons to help shape how I deal with the stresses and challenges of caregiving.

Rising above the life lessons, blunders, successes, and all the other experiences, however, is the knowledge that if something debilitating or devastating happens to me - then my family will suffer greatly. Recognizing the impossibility of living in a bubble and "even the best laid schemes of mice and men go often awry," I accepted that I couldn't insulate myself or my family from events beyond my control, but I could take steps towards quality physical and emotional health. With that said, I purposed to figure out what "caring for myself" looks like on a daily (often hourly) basis.

In this book, I present easy steps that I incorporate into my own life; steps to help me stay a little more healthy, focused, and even a bit more sane, while managing the unmanageable and containing the uncontainable. The last thing I want to read while "spinning plates," is a textbook that takes even more of my time. You know the type, written by someone who "thinks" about this stuff, but doesn't necessarily live it each and every day, so I have written in a way that I would want to read it, simple and to the point, filled with tips and lessons that readers can start today.

That's why I came up with the "1-2-30" plan. Three easy numbers that can remind me of simple things I can do to help reduce stress in the six major impact areas of a caregiver's life.

- Health
- Emotions
- Lifestyle
- Profession
- Money
- Endurance

I put them in that order to spell out: HELP ME

Boiling it all down, crying "HELP ME" is the first step toward improving your life as a caregiver. Individuals in trouble rarely get better without asking for help.

As a frightened young man faced with a nightmare, I did not know how to ask for help - or maybe I asked for help but not in a way that others could understand. Regardless, the years tuned my ears and heart a bit better - enhancing my abilities to hear the cries of my fellow caregivers, while also helping me to ask for help myself.

Picture with me again my younger self sitting alone outside my young wife's hospital room reading a medical chart for the first time, while covered with vomit, following the awful experience of watching her endure a seizure. The nurses all attended Gracie, but I was truly alone.

You may feel that way right now. If so, take a deep breath.

If you go down, what happens to the individual(s) depending upon you? How will that vulnerable person function if your finances, emotions, and health all crash? If you lost your job today, how well would your system function?

As to the person you are caring for, I appreciate their pain, challenges, situation, and/or disability; it's serious and it's significant. They will, however, be in even more difficult circumstances if you are not functioning as a healthy individual. Emotionally, physically, spiritually, financially, professionally - all of these areas require shoring up.

The purpose of this book is to grab you by the lapels, look you in the eye, and help you prioritize the six major areas of your life that feel the pressure of caregiving.

Sometimes, it helps to get a different perspective on a situation, in order for roles to be better defined. Let's start with a few qualifying questions:

• Did you create the condition your loved one endures?
• Can you cure their illness/condition?
• Can you control what is happening to them?

If you answered "yes" to these questions, then maybe this book is not for you. If you can create, cure, or control these types of life issues, then you don't need to worry about being a caregiver.

On the other hand, if you answered, "no" to those questions, you are well on your way to understanding your powerlessness and inability to alter or change the circumstances facing you as a caregiver, and that's a good thing.

Although my résumé as a caregiver is filled with amazing achievements, I must confess that, not only have I failed to "fix" the situation, I can't stop it from getting worse. In fact, I can't even slow it down.

Mulling over those facts, it dawns upon me that maybe I have a different role to play in this scenario.

If controlling it or curing it is impossible, then what is my job as a caregiver? After decades of putting on the cape and mask and acting like a superhero every time a medical crises pops up (often daily), I'm learning that my role is to love my wife, do the best I can, and grow as a healthy individual to the best of my abilities.

As a double-amputee who wears prosthetic limbs, Gracie falls. It breaks my heart when it happens, although I've put up as many safeguards as possible, I cannot guarantee that she never falls. I can, however, set as a goal to do my best to comfort her when she does, help her back up, brush her off, and dry the tears.

Gracie has received treatment by more than fifty-five doctors, and it is impossible for me to ensure that every doctor who treats her "gets it right every time." So my efforts then shift from physician management to personal management. The focus must be with a calm demeanor, thinking clearly, looking objectively at issues, and a peaceful state of mind. When things go sideways, I can better adapt and function with flexibility if I am not driven by unreasonable and unattainable goals.

Most of all, I'm learning to accept that my wife has a Savior, and I'm not Him.

As capable as I am, it is abundantly clear that I am powerless over her injuries and equally powerless to take away any of her considerable pain. I do, however, have an important role to play, but can only serve in that role if I am thinking and living in a healthy manner.

"But caregiving seems to consume all my time! How can I take care of me when I am exhausted every day?"

Do those complaints sound familiar?

That night in the hospital so long ago, I wouldn't have been able to process a "how-to" manual that required even more of the precious resources I spent every day. I needed something simple, attainable, practical, and able to do "right now."

What does that look like?

It looks like implementing *easy to accomplish* consistent steps to address the six major "HELP ME" impact areas affected by caregiving. Focusing on the health (emotional, physical, and financial) of the care giver is not selfish or self-centered, in fact, it is the opposite.

Exhausted caregivers make lousy caregivers.

If there is one thing a caregiver needs, it is mercy. Not just from others, but from within. We often whip ourselves mercilessly to achieve that which cannot be achieved, and in the process, we crash and burn, often miserably. By extending mercy to ourselves, we allow our weary hearts to rest. That rest enables us to better care for the ones we love. As we treat our worn-out hearts and bodies with mercy, we discover we can better receive kindness from others.

Erin stood steadfastly, but helplessly by the side of her infant son in intensive care. Dropping everything to get her child to the hospital as quick as possible, she realized too late that the shoes she wore were terrible for long periods of standing. As her emotional stress grew while watching her son struggling for his life, the ill-fitting shoes also increased her physical discomfort. Torn by the discomfort she felt in her feet and the fear of leaving her son even for a minute, Erin's stress and pain increased, until a thoughtful friend showed up with a pair of padded flip-flops that instantly provided comfort.

A simple pair of shoes helped a caregiver. Without lessening the stress or changing the circumstances of the crisis, this young mother's well-being improved, by accepting something practical from a kind soul who had either "been there," or at least had noticed the need.

Drawing upon a vast experience of "being there" and noticing the need, this book represents a practical aid for individuals struggling with conflicting emotions, weary bodies, and even sore feet, in the marathon of caregiving. By following the simple steps I've outlined, you love your charge more, because you are equipping yourself to bring your "A-game" to a situation that has little margin for error.

For many years, individuals have asked me what advice I have for caregivers. My reply is always the same, "Wear Comfortable Shoes ...it's a marathon not a sprint."

So, take a moment to slip on a pair of comfortable shoes, and let's walk together towards a healthier, relaxed, and more enjoyable daily life, while dealing with the constant challenges and often brutal realities, of caring for someone who suffers; someone whom you deeply love.

Health

Doctor, Doctor, Give Me the News,
I've Got a Bad Case of Lovin' You.
Robert Palmer

The demands of caregiving presume upon the health of the caregiver. With so much time spent addressing the needs of the patient, the weary body of the one pushing the wheelchair is often overlooked. Like saltwater affecting cars near the ocean, the stress of caregiving can erode the bodies (and minds) of caregivers.

- Caregivers under extreme stress have been shown to age prematurely. This level of stress can take as much as 10 years off a caregiver's life.[1]
- 23% of family caregivers caring for loved ones for 5 years or more report their fair or poor health.
- 58% have poor exercise habits
- 63% have poor diets
- 72% don't go to their doctor regularly [2]

These figures represent a time bomb for the families of caregivers. What happens to that family and the patient if the caregiver goes down?

Many years ago, I worked with a man named K.G. who took sole care of his beautiful wife after she was diagnosed with Alzheimer's. K.G. doted on her, fixed her hair, dressed her, and even helped her with makeup. As the disease progressed, she became increasingly frail and unable to perform even the most basic tasks. K.G. ramped it up even more, and threw himself into the task of caring for her, all while working full-time.

When I first met K.G., I was only a few years into caregiving. Although a thirty-year age gap existed between us, we shared a common bond, and I saw a small piece of myself in this gentle man caring for his sick wife.

Sadly, K.G. exhausted himself, and, in less than five years as a caregiver, he died of a heart attack. Less than a year before his death, he shared with me the one thing he feared the most: dying before his wife.

That scenario frightens caregivers, so let's just go ahead and talk about the elephant in the room: outliving our loved ones is a goal. If it all possible, I do not wish for my wife to live without my help, nor desire for our children to assume this responsibility.

How about you? Have you had this conversation with the ceiling during sleepless nights when no one can see the tears running down your face?

Even admitting this can cause many caregivers conflicting emotions, and counselors and therapists can probably pick it all apart and show us how messed up we may or may not be for having these thoughts, but these feelings and thoughts still weigh heavy upon us.

Gracie may have to live without me; things happen. If so, I've taken steps, including purchasing as much life insurance as I can afford. Should I die before my wife, our sons will be required to assume greater responsibilities. If so, we've raised outstanding young men who can handle the load. Regardless of those provisions, however, caregivers often work and plan to outlive their loved ones. In order to do so, however, we must take better care of ourselves physically. "Not dying" can't be the only goal, we need to keep ourselves as healthy as possible to minimize risks of stroke, diabetes, or other debilitating conditions that would compromise our abilities to care for our loved ones ...or worse, force the need for a caregiver ourselves.

Rather than concentrating on "not dying," the goal is to live well. Driven by my desire for simplicity, I came up with the three "E's" for improving the physical health of a caregiver.

EXERCISE

Doing physical things relieves an enormous amount of stress. I take martial arts three times a week. I love the class, and I work off a great deal of stress while doing something positive for myself. I also usually walk the dog for nearly two miles almost every day.

EATING

As a life-long Southerner (by God's grace) I do struggle with food issues. Everything seems fried in butter, and sweet tea is served by the gallon. Turning off "Southern," is not easy. I love good food, but I am learning to cut calories and improve energy levels by grabbing a banana rather than a candy bar, sushi instead of McDonalds. At the grocery store, picking up a bag of apples is vastly superior to fat-laden snacks and even a few small choices in purchasing and preparing food can result in positive results. When taking care of someone else (particularly while in crisis mode), we tend to grab whatever is closest and easiest. Unfortunately, those are usually NOT the best things for us.

Take it EASY

One of the most valuable things I've learned in *Hap-Kido*, the martial art I take, is breathing. I honestly never considered how important proper breathing is to stress release, energy levels, and even the ability to concentrate and focus. Sitting still and breathing 4 seconds in and controlled exhaling of 8 seconds out ...quickly melts away caregiver stress. Oxygenating the blood, while willing ourselves to calm down will result in increased energy and improved focus.

Remember, caregiving is a marathon not a sprint. With that in mind, use these 3 numbers when taking care of your own HEALTH:

1 - 2 - 30

1 Flu Shot

Do you have time to get the flu? Is your schedule wide open so that contracting the flu won't be a bother?

I didn't think so.

Although a flu shot may seem like a simple thing, it is a low-cost way of potentially avoiding a large problem. We've all suffered from the flu, but caregivers often don't have the built-in margin that allows for "sick-days."

The flu cannot only take you down, but potentially everyone you come in contact with, and vice-versa. Think about it: a flu shot - or risk 3-4 days of downtime to enjoy high fever, nausea, and other unpleasant symptoms? Our loved ones tend to have weaker immune systems, and are vulnerable to the flu. Who do you think has the greatest risk of catching it from them?

Spend $25 at your grocery store's pharmacy or check with your local state or city health department where they often provide them freely. Save yourself a heap of grief by getting a flu shot!

For a pastor or counselor meeting with a caregiver struggling with tough circumstances, asking whether or not the individual obtained a flu shot presents an easy way to reframe the conversation towards helping that caregiver make better health decisions. The circumstances of their loved one may be dire, but those challenges will not improve or take a vacation if the caregiver catches the flu.

Check with your doctor to ensure a flu shot is safe for you. Some individuals may exhibit adverse reactions. It's not for everyone, but for the vast majority of us, it provides an extra edge, however small, of avoiding an uncomfortable interruption into our already stretched life.

Note. There are always "tin-foil hat" types who think flu shots are a government conspiracy to prepare for an alien invasion. I suppose it's possible, but being abducted by Klingons would be worse if I had the flu, so I'm taking my chances with the shot.

2 Well Visits (including annual physical)

With an alarming 72% of caregivers not visiting their own doctor regularly, our country faces a time bomb of elderly and disabled individuals being left without a caregiver. Imagine the impact on our businesses, Medicare, churches, and the list goes on. Things such as prostate cancer, breast cancer, diabetes, stroke, heart disease, colon cancer, and a host of other illnesses can be treated, and even prevented, with early diagnosis and regular preventive care. A physical allows the caregiver to get out in front of their own health, so that they can stave off scary, but preventable diseases and issues.

Some caregivers cannot easily leave their charge, but that dilemma serves as an opportunity for the Church to help. By offering to care (or subsidize skilled care) for the loved one so the caregiver can make a doctor's appointment, the Church provides a huge help, while ensuring that the caregiver is receiving proper medical attention.

Churches across the world are full of individuals who want to help, but don't always know what to do or say to someone with a long-term issue. Churches excel at short-term traumas such as surgery, accident, and even funerals. We know what to do in those cases, and, often armed with food, we gather around the hurting to bring comfort, funds, and all sorts of help to individuals and families in need.

In the South, we're particularly good at that sort of thing.

"Hey, Earl, we heard you had your leg amputated - how about some macaroni and cheese!"

If you think that's an exaggeration, you're not a Southerner!

What about, however, when the trauma extends into months, years, or in my family's case …decades? Even the best intentioned individuals may grow weary after a helping-out for a couple of weeks, much less years. You can only take so many casseroles over to someone, before it gets old. Receiving meals from loving friends and family is wonderful, but eventually a caregiver has to learn to cook for himself.

Whereas church congregations see the need, the balancing act of managing their own lives makes it difficult for groups (or individuals) to maintain lengthy commitments to help. Intentions, however noble, do not often come with the resources needed for long-term care, and after a well-meaning start by many fellow church members, the caregiver often finds themselves isolated in their task. Initially, many church members express eagerness to help, but, as weeks stretch into months and years, the assistance dwindles.
Dr. Beryl G. Rosenberger
Pastor for fifty years and the author's father.

In not knowing what to say or do, well-meaning individuals may run the other way. Having a tangible way of helping, such as insuring that caregivers obtain an annual physical, becomes a relatively easy task that allows caring church members to get involved.

Whether scheduling volunteers to sit with the patient, or even paying for skilled care through the church's benevolent fund, the need for an annual physical for caregivers becomes the conversation starter for pastors, lay-leaders, friends, and family members who often may feel unsure on how to approach a caregiver with some sort of meaningful help.

"I just never know what to say" can now morph into, "Have you had a physical this year?" "Can I help get you to the doctor or sit with your mother while you visit your own doctor?"

Pastors know the ones struggling with these issues in the congregation, and, by addressing something as simple as an annual physical, now possess a simple, effective, and meaningful way of helping care for the caregiver.

Healthy individuals make for healthy families.

Healthy families make healthy churches

Healthy churches make health communities and nations.

Well Visit

Why wait for a year to discover high blood pressure, soaring cholesterol rate, or high triglycerides? When a caregiver visits the doctor, or just schedules lab work every six months (labs also come with an annual physical), then important data can be collected, giving a head start on potential issues. The warning bells for diabetes, prostate cancer, stroke, etc., should not wait for an annual physical.

If these types of services are unaffordable, most health departments, walk-in clinics, etc., have discounted or free services. Check with your insurance company to see if they offer better rates on well visits.

Keenly aware of the stress on me, my internist insists on regularly "put- ting eyeballs" on me, and I am deeply grateful for his friendship and expertise. I hate weighing, and I swear his nurse uses a knitting needle to draw blood, but seeing him every six months is critical for my health.

Again, this is where the church can play a huge role in a relatively simple task. It becomes almost a "compliance" issue for caregivers. Some caregivers want to whine. I've seen it, and done it. But by confronting the issues of caregivers head-on with a simple question, "Have you seen your doctor lately?"or "When's your next physical?" the concerns are reframed from serving as an "I don't know what to do" session, to being proactive about health, and empowering other caregivers to do the same.

Church committees want to help hurting families, but shy away from "throwing money" at the problem. By serving as a safety net for caregivers who cannot afford medical visits, churches, for relatively small costs, can ensure the caregivers in their congregations receive quality preventive health care services. Churches may want to work with physicians and nurses in the congregation and even set up some type of semi-annual clinic for members (and even nonmembers) who are caregivers. That does not mean churches take over America's health care system, but it does mean that pastoral care can expand into this arena without causing a church budget to suffer. The financial component of the church underwriting a doctor visit is simply a last resort. The first order of business is for the caregiver to regularly seek preventive health services.

Why all this focus on the church? Because the church has a mandate from its head: Jesus. Societies, in general, recognize the need to care for the sick and vulnerable members of communities, but the church has a mandate to do so, and the head of the church is serious about that mandate. Listen to Him in His own words:

"When the Son of Man comes in his glory, and all the angels with him, he will sit on his glorious throne. All the nations will be gathered before him, and he will separate the people one from another as a shepherd separates the sheep from the goats. He will put the sheep on his right and the goats on his left.

"Then the King will say to those on his right, 'Come, you who are blessed by my Father; take your inheritance, the kingdom prepared for you since the creation of the world. For I was hungry and you gave me something to eat, I was thirsty and you gave me something to drink, I was a stranger and you invited me in, I needed clothes and you clothed me, I was sick and you looked after me, I was in prison and you came to visit me.'

"Then the righteous will answer him, 'Lord, when did we see you hungry and feed you, or thirsty and give you something to drink? When did we see you a stranger and invite you in, or needing clothes and clothe you? When did we see you sick or in prison and go to visit you?'"

"The King will reply, 'Truly I tell you, whatever you did for one of the least of these brothers and sisters of mine, you did for me.'

"Then he will say to those on his left, 'Depart from me, you who are cursed, into the eternal fire prepared for the devil and his angels. For I was hungry and you gave me nothing to eat, I was thirsty and you gave me nothing to drink, I was a stranger and you did not invite me in, I needed clothes and you did not clothe me, I was sick and in prison and you did not look after me.'

"They also will answer, 'Lord, when did we see you hungry or thirsty or a stranger or needing clothes or sick or in prison, and did not help you?'

"He will reply, 'Truly I tell you, whatever you did not do for one of the least of these, you did not do for me.' "Then they will go away to eternal punishment, but the righteous to eternal life."   *Matthew 25:31-46 (NIV)*

Religion that is pure and undefiled before God, the Father, is this: to visit orphans and widows in their affliction, and to keep oneself unstained from the world.
James 1:27 (ESV)

<u>30 Minutes of Daily Exercise/Activity</u>

Daily exercise seems a no-brainer, but is hard for most people to do consistently. Jogging, swimming, walking, aerobics, martial arts, the options are lengthy. Pick one that works for you. My dog's bladder dictates the amount of daily walking I do, and although I often grumble about it, Mack gives me a good excuse to get outside and walk off some calories. Incorporating my Bluetooth earpiece, I use the time to catch up on calls, which helps the walk go more quickly.

Hap Kido serves as another physical outlet. Without any prior training, I walked into the Dojang (school), enrolled in this martial art and enjoy it immensely. My instructors also know the stresses on my life, and work with me to help bleed off some of the tension (sometimes literally, but it's my fault if my nose gets in the way of my instructor's fist). We don't do tournaments or things like that, and although it is a self-defense program, I also find wonderful life applications through this art.

In referencing the movie *Sho-Gun*, I told my instructors that they should make a movie about me called, "Sho-Nuff!" (After wiping the blood off the back of my head and resuming my place in class, I quit making jokes to guys who wear black-belts.)

I'm not an athlete, nor am I in great shape. I used to be but life, time, and caregiving all wreak havoc on our bodies. Moderation is the key; caregiving is a marathon not a sprint. Years of inactivity and bad diet are not quickly reversed. Take it easy, but steady. Every step we take, even walking the dog, leads to more healthy choices.

But remember to put on comfortable shoes.

I told you this would be practical, and now you can take your first step towards surviving and thriving as a caregiver, and it's as easy as *1-2-30*.

Emotions

It's difficult to think anything but pleasant thoughts
while eating a homegrown tomato.
Lewis Grizzard

Arguing over whether or not the glass
is half-empty or half-full is pointless
...the bottom line is that the bartender cheated you.
I read this somewhere, and it made me laugh.

Caregiving takes a MASSIVE toll on your beating heart - and your "person" heart. The stress and dynamics of a relationship filled with constant medical and caregiving challenges quickly (and easily) overpower even the strongest of family and marital bonds. Arguments and resentment often seem ever-present, particularly in marriages where one of the partners is ill, but not necessarily cognitively impaired. Marriages in families living with a disabled family member currently have a divorce rate hovering around ninety percent.

To be fair - the divorce rate for most celebrity marriages soars to about 187% (factoring in multiple marriages).

Serving as a caregiver guarantees the following feelings:
• Fear
• Obligation

- Guilt
- Heartache
- Anger
- Turmoil

(The anagram spells FOGHAT because I like 70's music)

Caregivers bounce all over the emotional map between compassion and frustration, obligation and commitment. The lines get so blurry at times, that caregivers often find themselves operating out of intense Fear, Obligation, and Guilt ...which leads to Heartache, Anger, and Turmoil.

Get it? In a FOG with a HAT ? FOG HAT!?

How do ships and planes navigate through a FOG? They use a GPS (Global Positioning System). Why not people?

- **FEAR**
- **OBLIGATION**
- **GUILT**

Can be navigated by using a **GPS**

- **GRACE**
- **PURPOSE**
- **STEWARDSHIP**

Let's start with **<u>GUILT</u>**

Caregivers struggle mightily with guilt. Being able to easily get up and walk while our loved one can't, jumping into the car to run errands while he/she is stuck at home, standing up in the shower while they have to use shower benches, and/or not living with chronic pain - it seems virtually every scenario contains a guilt component. Parents of disabled children wrestle with intense guilt over a disabled son or daughter who did not ask to be born into a life filled with disability and suffering.

In addition, caregivers make mistakes, some of them grievous; we are human beings after all. We trip over the same sins and vices that others do, but the immense pressure of caregiving often compresses our learning curve.

Most individuals experience a "slow growth" into maturity and life crises. Caregivers find ourselves on the express lane towards managing crises, dealing with life and death issues, and a lengthy list of other intense scenarios. The stress from the non-stop barrage dulls our senses, and even eats away at our moral compass. When we do fail, guilt from the failure gnaws at the soul and mercilessly flogs us to work hard, deny ourselves more, and slam additional pressures on an already stress-filled life.

That is no way for anyone to live, and certainly not caregivers.

In Gracie's book, we share some of my failures along this journey. The guilt and shame of those things nearly pushed me into insanity (granted, a lot of pushing wasn't needed, but I digress). After a long time, I finally decided to deal with those issues properly. Through the process, I learned that God didn't go through all the trouble to send his Son to die on the cross to bear my guilt and shame, only to have me pick it back up again and wear it like a fur coat on a hot July day.

> My sin, oh, the bliss of this glorious thought!
> My sin, not in part but the whole,
> Is nailed to the cross, and I bear it no more,
> Praise the Lord, praise the Lord, O my soul!
> It Is Well With My Soul
> *Horatio Spafford*

While we're on the subject, I make no apologies for my Christian faith. If you want to endure something like my wife and I have by trusting in something else, that's your decision, but I would offer this brief snippet about one of the greatest minds of the 20th century, C.S. Lewis.

C.S. Lewis walked into a room where some of his friends had been having a discussion for several hours. He asked what they were talking about. They said, "We have been discussing what makes Christianity different than all other religions."

C.S. Lewis said, "That's easy. It's grace." And he walked out of the room.

He was right. A single word captures the difference between Christianity and all other religions.

Grace

Red Like Blood: Confrontations with Grace
- Joe Coffey and Bob Bevington

Grace replaces guilt.

What a beautiful word, "Grace." I often state that I needed grace so much in my life that I married a woman named "Grace."

Guilt is a terrible taskmaster, and destroys any relationship - particularly those involving caregivers. Remember, guilt comes from many sources, not just big-time sins that get great press.

- Guilt of the patient living a life filled with pain and/or from a wheel- chair, while you walk around freely.
- Guilt from having a child born with a disability.
- Guilt from an injury or negligence you inadvertently caused that left a loved one with a permanent disability.

Caregivers can't effectively live and serve others with that kind of guilt, so it is necessary to apply grace to those guilty feelings when they surface. By consistently reminding ourselves of how God's grace covers our sins (not so we have a license to keep repeating them), we discover that guilt no longer whips us into a lathered frenzy. Grace frees us to love and serve from a clean and guilt-free heart. Sometimes, remembering God's grace is not day to day, but rather minute to minute.

If a lifestyle of sin and destruction consistently plague the caregiver, those issues need to be dealt with through counseling with either a pastor or a trained mental health expert. From experience, I know the extreme agony of trying to serve as a caregiver while maintaining a life filled with a destructive coping mechanism. When caregivers turn to sex, alcohol, or drugs, the end result of using any of these (or other) harmful escapes is a fractured caregiver and additional strain on an already fractured family.

Of all the topics the church can effectively address with authority, guilt remains at the top. The church is structured to properly and effectively deal with guilt.

Note: I love the church and am grateful for the one I attend. Sadly, too many clergy and church folks use guilt to leverage control over others. Let's face it, some people are arrogant, self-righteous, and just full of themselves, and will, to satisfy their own need for power and affirmation, say and do things that are harmful to others.

Given that, try to avoid highly religious individuals who spend a great deal of time giving answers to life's issues.

We live in a fallen, broken world where bad things happen, often without a fairy-tale ending. That won't change until Christ returns.

I don't know God's reasons for not divinely removing the challenges and suffering we live with, and neither does anyone else. Any pastor, church leader, etc., who tells you they do ...will make up stuff about other things, as well.

FEAR
There is no fear in love; but perfect love
casts out fear, because fear involves torment.
1 John 4:18 New King James Version

Fear involves torment. What a powerful statement. When serving as a caregiver, it seems fear constantly lurks around every door.

- What happens if...?
- How can we afford...?
- What are we going to do...?

I've lost count of how many times I've covered my head with a pillow or crawled under the blankets trying to shut out all the fear racing around in my mind. Bills, surgeries, a wife groaning and screaming in pain, seizures, respiratory arrest - the list seems endless. Never knowing what's coming around the corner, I still find myself flinching before remembering to calm down and not operate in fear.

Gripped by fear is a lousy way to live.

Staying with the GPS theme, caregivers can replace fear with purpose. Regardless of how crazy it may sound, we can begin to see purpose weaving through ugly suffering. The Bible tells us this. Brilliant thinkers tell us this. For me, a lesson that stands out more than others is one of the more dramatic times I literally saved Gracie's life. Recounted in her book, I'll let her share it:

During the summer of 2003, my husband, Peter, and I flew to Washington, DC for our first trip to one of the most famous hospitals in America. Walking into the historic "Red Cross Building" on post at Walter Reed, I suddenly felt as if step- ping into our country's history. Beautifully paneled, the old building continues to voicelessly count the wounded warriors passing through one of our nation's most treasured military posts. Only the hardest and most callous hearts remained unaffected when visiting the campus of Walter Reed. Every building, every street, and every garden speaks the names of men and women in uniform who walked, or were carried, through the gates.

"There are so many amputees out there," was my first thought as I looked out across the audience of soldiers that night. Only recently enduring a difficult operation myself, I felt weak and unqualified to stand in front of anyone. Looking around, I paused to once again appreciate God's perfect plan, as I quickly realized that the soldiers I came to visit didn't need me to be well and feeling strong; they needed to hear from someone who spent long hours in a hospital - while depending upon God for each one of those hours.

Looking at the assembled crowd, I couldn't help but be surprised at the dinner. Outback Steakhouse catered the affair, and served the meal buffet style. (If you ever have the opportunity to eat a buffet catered by Outback - I heartily recommend it!) Seated at my table, I looked around at many young men and women missing limbs, other's pushing IV poles, and still others in wheelchairs. Puzzled, I asked Peter why the army would allow a buffet for wounded soldiers, many of whom could not even walk; I have a problem with buffets myself.

As the question left my lips, I immediately learned the answer: officers, celebrities, and more importantly, the senators from the Republican Senate Caucus assembled there, all worked together to serve these young men and women.

At our table, we dined with Senator and Mrs. Chuck Grassley from Iowa and then Senator Norm Coleman from Minnesota. At my left sat a handsome man who looked familiar, but I couldn't place him. Peter stepped in and saved me from embarrassment when he introduced me to former NFL quarterback and now sports announcer, Boomer Esiason.

I watched Boomer and Senator Coleman repeatedly hop up to help each new young person being wheeled into the auditorium; Boomer even offered to get me a plate.

Looking around the room, I recognized more and more celebrities, athletes, and political figures carrying a plate and drink to a waiting soldier. With egos checked at the door, each of these individuals displayed such humility and genuine gratitude to the young men and women bearing brutal scars from the war on terror.

Watching senators serve wounded warriors, stands out as one of the most meaningful memories of my life. With no media present, I'm sorry our country lacked the ability to witness such an event.

As the evening progressed, Senator Santorum presided as master of ceremonies, and he introduced speaker after speaker. Tommy Lasorda brought the house down with his humor and great stories from coaching. Even as all these speakers shared from the podium, however, I noticed the crowd continued to talk and eat, and generally remain boisterous.

At the close of the evening, Senator Santorum asked for everyone's attention and introduced us. The room grew quiet for the first time that evening, and my nerves once again felt rattled.

Leaning on Peter and taking Senator Santorum's hand, I climbed the four or five stairs leading to the platform. Even that act drew the undivided attention of the audience, particularly the wounded warriors gathered up front.

Walking on stage in a skirt, my uncovered prosthetic legs clearly visible to the assembled crowd, I couldn't help but notice how many amputees were assembled in front of me. Young men and women, not much older than our son, Parker, at the time, with scars, casts, and maimed limbs looking all too familiar, sat in wheel- chairs in front of the stage; each of them staring intently at my legs, watching my every move.

Over the years, I've discovered that if Peter will open up our appearances and kind of "break the ice" it helps settle me down. I never know how to "start," and usually verbally trip and fall right out of the gate.

Hearing him smoothly convey an introduction to our part in the event, I quickly whipped my head towards him when hearing his voice break. In all our years speaking and performing, I don't ever remember Peter choking up on stage, but I certainly understood why.

The sight of so many soldiers wounded in service of our country creates an almost reverent atmosphere. Until recently, these soldiers, some barely out of high school, enjoyed life at an absolute peak physical condition. Trained by the greatest military in the history of the world, words such as honor, duty, determination, stamina, and achievement served as hallmarks of their everyday lives. Could they transition those same traits into this dreadful new set of circumstances?

The celebrities spoke from their heart, and gave encouragement to the audience; particularly Coach Lasorda. Although desiring to also offer encouragement, my role clearly involved something else: practical hope. I served as the lone speaker that night who understood the journey ahead for many of them. At the beginning of our country's war on terror, these wounded warriors were the first of their type since Vietnam - and they now saw a little of their future as I walked across the stage wearing state-of-the art prosthetic limbs.

Just by watching me stride onto the platform, those who were missing limbs observed the possibilities. With each step of my prosthetic feet, I felt the eyes of extremely scared young men and women who seemed to hold their breath with every footstep. Seeing me with a husband, the women with maimed bodies causing them to feel less than beautiful realized a boyfriend waited somewhere for them. Hearing about our sons, they also realized a family still remained in their future. Lost limbs do not automatically mean lost hope.

35

As Peter took his place at the piano, I paused for a moment to look at the crowd. Ignoring the famous individuals gathered there, I instead turned my gaze to the anxious but eager faces clustered near the stage. Many of them struggled to understand the purpose of the wounds suffered halfway around the world. For two decades, I wrestled with purpose in injuries; knowing that if some meaning or good comes from wounds ...the healing often becomes a little easier. Wounded at about the same age as these "kids," I knew the questions lurking in their hearts. Looking at me, they saw possibilities; now, I needed to help direct their eyes to purpose.

"Three weeks ago I had my sixty-sixth operation in twenty years. In my room after the surgery, I unexpectedly went into respiratory arrest and the code team had to be called to help me start breathing again. It was Peter who saved my life. He was sitting right beside me when I stopped breathing, and quickly got the right people to come resuscitate me. He wasn't off somewhere watching TV or working a deal on his cell phone, he was right beside me; right where God wanted him. I'm alive today because he was where he was supposed to be.

Americans are alive today because you were where you were supposed to be. You helped keep this war away from our streets, schools, offices and malls. You saved the lives of perfect strangers all across the country because you were where you were called to be."

The room grew even quieter. Peter observed senators locked in their own political battles in dealing with the war on terror, listening intently.

"I fell asleep at the wheel—a stupid mistake. God continues to redeem that event, but there is no honor in my injuries. My

36

mistake cost me my legs; you offered yours. Your injuries have honor because you won them fighting for the precious God-given gift of freedom."

Signaling Peter to play the introduction, I sang his song "We Will Stand." Peter wrote this song for me as an expression of his desire to care for me. Writing these lyrics, he expressed his heart to me, and now I shared them with the precious soldiers gathered at Walter Reed Army Medical Center.

Finishing the song, I looked down at the young men and women gathered in wheelchairs as they applauded. I believe they liked the song, but their applause reached past my performance as a singer …and validated the courage to face life with a maimed body. In me, they caught a hint of themselves a few years down the road; hope still remained for a meaningful life …even with amputations. They clapped and cheered for every individual who refuses to be defined by wounds, disfigurement, and disability.

Afterwards we all clustered together; wounded individuals sharing a moment as members of an exclusive club. Fascinated by my state-of-the art components, they peppered me with questions, wanted to touch the legs, and discussed so many more things involved with limb loss.

"Can we get feet like yours?"

"Do you get in the water with those?"

"Do they have a lot of cushion when you step?"

We stayed for an hour longer, until everyone had to leave. Senator Orrin Hatch of Utah and Senator Richard Shelby of Alabama tried to greet me afterwards, but couldn't reach past the soldiers. Both of them turned to Peter and smiled, graciously asking him to give me their regards.

"We're not important; she's right where she needs to be," Senator Hatch humbly told Peter.

From *Gracie-Standing With Hope*
© 2010 Liberty University Press

In that hall at Walter Reed Army Medical Center, an audience full of wounded warriors, celebrities, and politicians witnessed *fear* yield to *purpose*. Oddly, looking for and acknowledging God's purpose is often when we feel gripped by fear. The pain is not lessened, the crisis doesn't immediately stop; but the fear gives way to trust in a loving God who reaches into the most horrific of circumstances and pulls out something amazing.

OBLIGATION is another horrible taskmaster, and a poor motivator for caregiving. When we feel obligated to do and care for another, we often store up massive amounts of bitterness and resentment. After a while, nothing that our loved one does "is right" and the building resentment can erupt into painful outbursts which add more misery to an already miserable situation.

When feeling the crushing impact of feeling obligated, we can re- member that the "S" in "GPS" stands for stewardship. If we are stewards of our loved one's caregiving issues, then it doesn't belong to us. We can only do our best, and the rest has to be up to God. Even then, we know we will fail, but God's grace covers those failures, as well.

Although I have certainly hurt Gracie's heart and done sinful things in my life, I did not cause her injuries, or the subsequent pain and loss she lives with. She's broken. I didn't break her. I can't fix her. As a steward, I can love her and care for her, but ultimately, I am not responsible for "fixing" her.

This may sound basic, even cold, but let's go a bit deeper.

Truthfully, I have never even heard of someone with my caregiving credentials, but, have I fixed anything? Honestly, no. Gracie's pain and injuries lie beyond any of my abilities. Yes, I've saved her life, helped her through many crises, and battled mightily on her behalf, but it is not enough, nor is it sustainable.

Grappling with these issues philosophically, I have to ask, "What's my purpose and role in this?" I certainly can't fix it, so where's this going? Is the goal to eliminate pain and suffering?

If so, then we better prepare ourselves for disappointment, because that is a "God-sized" job. We caregivers sometimes (mistakenly) convince ourselves that it is up to us to fix the problem. Yet with all our efforts, we cannot avoid pain, loss, and even tragedy.

Pain is inevitable; joy, however, is not. As "caregivers who are stewards," we put the burden of "solution" where it belongs: on God. This is His problem, not ours. Doing so releases us to love without obligation or the burden of responsibility for something that does not belong to us. We may grieve over loss, but we still remain powerless to fix certain things. Recognizing that powerlessness grows from initially seeming like impotence, to a freeing acceptance that relieves us of the burden of being in charge.

Gracie has a Savior, and I'm not Him.

If I believe that all of this is somehow up to me, I will, in a vain attempt to fix the unfixable, push myself to despair.

After decades of trying to force solutions, I have to admit that my behavior worsened and my relationships suffered. That admission led me to a support group where I continue to gain the courage and wisdom to stop trying to fix that which is not mine to fix. (I have to go a lot!) We caregivers often like to swoop in and rescue, but sometimes we need to tip-toe in and just "be."

Gracie's circumstances are beyond my abilities …and above my pay- grade. I am a steward, not a fixer. At the end of the day, if I have been faithful to do what was mine to do, and resisted leaning in and meddling where I don't belong, then I can put my head down peacefully, and wake up the next day rested and ready to face the challenges waiting there. When I fail to do that, then the next best thing is to quickly make amends.

Think of the millions of lives that have gained sobriety and peace with this simple prayer:

God, grant me the serenity
to accept the things I cannot change
The courage to change the things that I can
And the wisdom to know the difference.

The extreme pressures and stress of caregiving play havoc with our emotions and often leave us wandering in a FOG full of fear, obligation, and guilt. The only way out is with a GPS using Grace, Purpose, and Stewardship.

Use these 3 numbers when taking care of your own emotions:

1-2-30

- 1 counseling session per month
- 2 support groups per month
- 30 days in Church per year

1 counseling session per month

Whether a psychiatrist, psychologist, social worker, or pastor, caregivers need a trained professional to meet with them and help sort through some of the craziness. If you don't know one, check with your work- place and inquire about an Employee Assistance Program (EAP) that is offered freely to workers. The EAP visits are often limited to a half- dozen, and then a plan coalesces to transition to long-term counseling that will become the employee's responsibility. I've taken advantage of those services many times, and I heartily recommend it to others. Licensed clinical social workers (I like to call them the "work horses of the counseling industry") offer a tremendous source of help at usually affordable fees. Insurance may or may not cover visits to counselors, and if they do, it is often only a percentage. One visit a month, however, is well worth the fee. (Keep your receipts for tax purposes.)

Again, this is an area where the church can excel. Pastors/chaplains can be a great resource for caregivers, but they may not always be best for long-term care. Since caregivers rarely deal with short-term issues, long-term counseling is advised. Clergy members, however, are usually well acquainted with qualified counselors, and can help refer and transition the long-term counseling needs to those individuals.

A benevolence committee can legitimately get behind underwriting the fees of a counselor to spend time once a month (at least) with someone dealing with long-term caregiving issues - but who may not be able to afford the costs. Again, no committee at any church or organization wants to simply throw money at a problem, but if the expense is qualified in a specific expenditure such as a monthly counseling for someone who cannot afford it, then it helps the church know that it is tangibly helping someone who is dealing with an impossible situation.

Note of caution: If a pastor or his designee is too busy to meet with a caregiver facing chronic issues in his church, I would suggest that it is time to find another church - they may be too busy to meet with God, as well.

2 Support Group Meetings Per Month

Ideally, those support group meetings would be two per week, but the schedule of a caregiver is often hectic. There are many types of support groups for family members of the mentally ill, Alzheimer's, and all sorts of things. Larger churches in your area may offer a non-denominational "caregiver support group." Check a couple of them out until you find the one that connects with your circumstances …and then stick with it. The purpose of attending support groups is not to change the issues causing us stress (which we are powerless to change), but rather to help us more healthily respond to the extreme challenges in our lives.

30 Days in Church

Thirty days in church each year does not allow for every Sunday (or Saturday) but it does put us in the pew 2.5 times per month (average), and allows our faith to be strengthened while also connecting us to a loving church body. Isolation continues as a terrible consequence of caregiving, so connecting to a quality group of loving people becomes imperative.

As caregivers, attending church each time the doors are open is impossible. The goal is not to put ourselves under some type of system of rules, but rather to help set attainable and realistic targets.

Again, you are welcome to be an atheist and deal with this stuff, but I don't recommend it. I can't even say, "Good luck with that!" to an atheist, since "luck" implies something other than random chance. So, to any atheists who read this part and reject it, well, "have at it!"

Tips to look for in a church: Stay away from "health and wealth" churches that consistently portray God as a Santa Claus type and a have a "vending machine theology." (Put money in, make your selection, and get what you want.) Also, avoid church folk who tell you they know why we (and our loved ones) suffer.

Heck, I know why Gracie suffers - she had a car wreck. The question I wrestle with is "Why doesn't God heal her?" That question has caused more insomnia than anything else in my life, and I have yet to find an answer that makes me want to smack my forehead and say, "Ohhhh ... that's why! I feel better now!"

Given all the hours I've logged with counselors, pastors, and with God, I land on the premise that if I still struggle with understanding suffering and God's provision, then I am going to be a bit wary and skittish about bombastic individuals who purport to know all the answers; especially if their life isn't filled with brutal challenges. (Have you noticed that people who live with great suffering tend to express more humility about "having answers"?)

We're not going to know all the answers until we get to Heaven. Anyone who tells you they do - will lie about other things, too.

"We must speak where the Scripture speaks; we must keep silent where it is silent." *John Calvin*

The Bible doesn't lay out every answer to every question, nor does it cover every tragic scenario.

What it does do, however, is clearly describe in great detail a sovereign, all-wise, loving God who bore the entire stench and judgment of man's sin upon His own Son. That same God weaves HIS purpose into even the most horrific circumstances, and one day we will see it made plain before us. When we do, every knee will bow and every tongue confess that Jesus Christ is Lord.

That knowledge has sustained uncounted millions through brutal realities, and can sustain caregivers, as well.

Given that, churches are still filled with broken people, and even the best of churches will have dysfunction. A flawed church doesn't excuse our absence, but caregivers (and others) would benefit from using great wisdom when selecting a church. I make it a rule to avoid church folks who do the following:

- Talk a lot about "getting something from God," instead of focusing on what we've already received.
- Seem to have an answer for everything , which usually involves "something you have to do better."
- Spend more time talking about "getting your breakthrough" rather than focusing on the need for repentance, and trusting God's provision - even in suffering.
- Preach sermons that would make better self-help speeches. I like motivational seminars as much as the next guy, but sermons need to preach the Gospel, the plan of salvation, and point to Christ.

Motivational messages don't hold up in the long run. The Gospel, however, sustains through all the world can lob. Rather than hopping around to find someone to give me the next "feel-good" and motivational-evangelical gimmick, we seek out companionship and fellowship in our challenges; relationships that build us up with sustainable truth.

God's plan and purpose in all of this is greater than our understanding. We are caregivers, not consultants. Focusing on what God DID do that we CAN understand, however, helps strengthen our faith and bolster courage. I know that one day I'll be in Heaven with Him …and all of my questions will be answered. In the meantime, I choose to hang on to what Paul said in his epistle to the Romans:

And we know that all things work together for good to those who love God to those who are called according to his purpose.
Romans 8:28 New King James Version

Peter and Gracie

Walter Reed Army Medical Center
Photo Courtesy: Billy Graham Evangelistic Association

Lifestyle

There cannot be a crisis next week.
My schedule is already full.
Henry Kissinger

Caregiving not only affects the caregiver's health and emotions, but their lifestyle as well.

- 20 hours per week is the average number of hours family caregivers spend caring for their loved ones.
- 13% of family caregivers are providing 40 hours of care a week or more. [2]

Forget trying to plan a vacation as a caregiver, it's usually a major event just to go to see a movie! Starting out each morning anticipating the "crisis du jour," we caregivers frequently throw our hands up in exasperation at trying to schedule and reschedule things. With the daily bombardment of medical and caregiving issues, is it possible to carve out some things to improve our overall well-being? It doesn't require a trip to Italy, or an exotic island beach. Is it too much to ask for a quiet cot in the corner with no one bothering us for a couple of hours?!

In the context of caregiving, feeling better about ourselves is not a selfish and egocentric pursuit. A more relaxed, self-confident, and emotionally calm caregiver almost guarantees that his/her charge will receive better and more consistent care. If the loved one is not cognitively impaired, the relationship can even deepen when a caregiver feels rested and refreshed.

Every caregiver needs time off, but guilt, obligation, and fear often shelve breaks. Getting away is not easy, and it may have to be in small but consistent chunks of time. Carving out "downtime" is paramount to serving as a good caregiver. I know your loved one suffers - so does mine, but you and I can't change that fact - nor will we help them if by driving ourselves until we're nothing but a husk.

Given that, three things come to mind that each caregiver can immediately implement to enhance their lifestyle with minimum (if any) costs - yet reap tremendous benefits to lighten the load: *Laugh, Leisure, and Leave.*

LAUGH

*Hearty laughter is a good way to jog internally
without having to go outdoors.*
Norman Cousins

Although humor sometimes serves as a bit of a shield to stave off painful feelings, genuinely funny moments in even

50

the direst of circumstances continue to surprise (and delight) me.

I once heard a story about a beloved church leader from a small, rural congregation who passed away following a long illness. As a tribute and gift to the widow, the music minister offered to enlist the choir to sing the man's favorite song at the funeral. Inquiring from the bereaved woman, the music minister was surprised to hear her name her husband's favorite song as "Jingle Bells."

Double checking with her, she emphatically stated that his favorite song was indeed, "Jingle Bells," and expressed great gratitude that the choir offered to sing her deceased husband's much loved song at the service.

Recognizing that his offer committed him, the music minister assembled the choir, and, with sales skills rivaling the best salesman on the planet, convinced the church choir to perform "Jingle Bells" at the funeral, which took place in June.

After the eulogy, the choir stood up and belted out, "Dashing through the snow, in a one-horse open sleigh ..."

As the assembled crowd of family and friends looked on with puzzlement, while dressed in summer attire, the embarrassed, but committed, choir sat down feeling as if they did the best they could for the grieving widow.

At the grave side, the music minister passed by the man's wife, took her hand, and once again gave his sincere condolences. Tearfully thanking him for the music, she quizzically looked at the music minister and remarked, "I loved all the hymns and songs, but why did you all sing "Jingle Bells"?

Wide-eyed, he replied, "You stated it was his favorite song."

With a sad, but sweet grin, she put her hand to her mouth, and laughed. "Ohhhh, I am so sorry. I meant, "Golden Bells!"

Sometimes humor meets tragedy in strange places. Our challenge is to expect and enjoy it.

Over the years I've met quite a few comedians, and each of them makes a living seeing what many call tragedy or crises through a "funny-shaped" lens. As a writer, I try to incorporate as much humor and wit as possible in all I write, simply because it's less boring to me. People often ask me who inspires me as a writer. I usually enthusiastically state, "Lewis!" With admiration and raised eyebrows, many cerebral types respond, "C.S.?"

"No ...Grizzard!"

In certain circles, my reply usually results in confused or disappointed faces, but I discovered two kinds of people: those who like Lewis Grizzard, and those who don't know better.

I love to read, and I've gone through my share of C.S. Lewis, Dietrich Bonhoeffer, Francis Schaeffer, and other great Christian thinkers, but I have to be honest; the profoundness in the simple descriptions of human nature that Grizzard captures still amazes me. He packs into a couple of paragraphs what many authors take chapters to write. If reading *Elvis Is Dead and I Don't Feel So Good Myself*, or *Shoot Low Boys, They're Riding Shetland Ponies* makes me less of an academic, well so be it!

Lewis Grizzard, by the way, was a great American!

With a vast spectrum of comedic tastes to choose from, pick one that makes your sides split. Seinfeld to Foxworthy, Andy Griffith to Tim Allen; a host of comedians compete for our amusement, so let's take them up on it! Watch a funny movie, catch a stand-up comedian on television, and/or read a hilarious author. In do so, you can feel the stress melt off your heart. Caregiving is serious business; but life can be whimsical; go with it and lighten up a bit.

Laughter gives us distance. It allows us to step back from an event, deal with it and then move on.
Bob Newhart

LEISURE

Have some fun, take a break. Sometimes it is possible to have fun with the person you are caring for, but most of the time, even the "fun things" become work for caregivers who have to help a loved one have fun.

I don't need over the top entertainment, I'm pretty good with a Louis L'Amour western, and, truthfully, of all the caregivers I've met in my life, 100% them just want a quiet, restful place to be alone with their thoughts and/or not have to worry about someone else for a brief moment.

When I get a break, I feel time slows down for me. Although I travel a lot, I don't mind it so much when I'm not taking care of another person. The TSA seems nicer, airplane food tastes better (what little there is nowadays), sunsets are prettier, birds sing more, and the list goes on. It's not that I am happier *per se*, but rather I slow down and enjoy the little things and the quiet moments.

The abilities and stability of caregivers increase with regular rest and leisure. Even God took a Sabbath rest. Free time means just that: FREE time. It is our time to do what relaxes us and improves our state of mind and body. Wrapping our entire beings into our role as caregivers, taxes the love we have for our charges, and saps our identity, creativity, and even sometimes even our ability to focus.

Now, before anyone uses that axiom as an excuse to head to strip clubs, bars, and so forth, vices don't improve one's state of mind or body. In fact, it does the opposite. Abusing alcohol, illicit sex, and recreational drug use are not antidotes for the stress caregivers feel. They will not only compound the tension and anxiety, but can also destroy relationships and ultimately our lives.

LEAVE

"You Deserve a Break Today, So Get Up and Get Away ..."
McDonald's

Honestly, we have to get some space. It doesn't have to be at McDonald's necessarily, but we caregivers need to get away on a regular basis.

For the first 40 surgeries Gracie endured under my watch, I used to stay nearly around the clock with her at the hospital.

Big mistake.

Before we married, Gracie underwent her twenty-first surgery, but it was the first one with me. Although newly engaged, I had not yet "gotten my feet wet" as a caregiver, and several family members watched me to see how I would "handle" the pressure. The surgeon met with the family following the procedure, and assured everyone that she was fine, but would be in recovery for some time. Breathing a sigh of relief, we all smiled at each other, until I did the unthinkable: I went to a movie to blow off some steam and relax.

I later learned of the gasps and disapproval by some of the women gathered around. One of them was the mother-in-law of one of my relatives, and had no "skin in the game," but she felt it her duty to properly evaluate my behavior, and hold up a scorecard as if she served as an Olympic judge during a diving contest.

It didn't help that she was also a "holier than thou" type. You know the ones, they have a bumper sticker on their Cadillac that states "My Other Car Is a Chariot of Fire!"

While I took a break and enjoyed myself at the movie, the judgment piled higher, as the group seemed to revel in how I "just wasn't up to the task."

A friend pulled me aside to share all this with me, and I mistakenly acted contrite to get into good graces with everyone. My instincts, however, were exactly right, and I wish I'd listened to them more. Gracie had a whole team of nurses and doctors, and only required my help AFTER those professionals were no longer available. For a one-time event like a broken arm or something, this principle doesn't necessarily apply. Issues stretching over years, however, are a "game changer." When help is present, take advantage of it by leaving the premises and allowing fresh air into your body and soul. Caregivers require regular breaks - preferably without being criticized by others.

While I'm at it, I developed a policy about people who criticize how I handle caregiving issues and the decisions I make as a caregiver: *The length of time I will listen to someone criticize, is in direct proportion to how much time the critic spends helping.*

If you like that policy, you are welcome to use it, and I hope it helps stave off those who simply want to carp.

When taking care of your lifestyle, the three "L's" become an easy tool to remind yourself to take it easy: "LAUGH, LEISURE, LEAVE." As with every area of a caregivers life, I also have a **1-2-30 reminder.**

1 "something" for yourself every week.

Catch a movie, golf, go to a museum, ride your bike, go fishing, etc. Do one special something for yourself every week. Sometimes I like catching a movie or a good book, but other times I find myself alone in the sanctuary at our church playing the piano for an hour or two.

If you need someone to sit with your loved one while you take a break, call your church. If your church won't help with that, ask a friend (and then change churches).

2 weeks' annual vacation from caregiving.

Most likely, you can't do this at one time, but if by spreading it over the year, it becomes possible; break it down, and it is roughly a day/night off every month. Yes, it may mean asking for help from others. That's where the church offers great assistance. Church leaders can help find a person who could help, or even find some money to pay for skilled care of some type (RN, LPN, CAN, etc.) to stay overnight while you get out of town for a night or so. Most services that offer something like that run around $15-20 per hour (depending upon location). Although that sounds like a lot of money, there are ways around the costs. The challenge for caregivers is to make the commitment to care for ourselves, and watch the resources appear. Experience teaches me that it's not a lack of resources, but a lack of resourcefulness that prohibits progress.

Churches are full of professionals, students, young people, retired members, and so forth, who can volunteer. Most caregivers have some sort of family structure to help share the load, but for those who do not, a church family becomes imperative. It is important for the church to bring its considerable resources to the table by helping with extreme caregiver situations such as single mothers with a special needs child, elderly spouses caring for each other, one person dealing with a catastrophic illness over lengthy periods of time, etc.

Money of course is a consistent issue, but the local church body is a network of professionals and volunteers who can bring a wealth of aid to any situation. A well-informed pastoral staff knows the ones in the church who are struggling with long-term and/or extreme caregiving, and can connect the right resources, ask better questions, help map out a plan of care, and provide a much needed support network that targets long-term care issues.

30 minutes a day with something humorous

Television is full of sitcoms (some of them stupid; others profane and disgusting), but somewhere in all of that programming, there are laughs waiting for you. Go get them. If television is not your thing, load comics onto your I-pod, and listen to them while going for a walk, and kill two birds with one stone (or, like Chuck Norris, you can kill two stones with one bird!)

For the frugal, your local library has all kinds of things just waiting for you to check them out! Find something that makes you laugh for thirty minutes a day! I download to my phone a free app of jokes that just make me cry with laughter. Granted, amusing me is not difficult, but the benefit is a better disposition and a little lighter outlook. Everyone has a sense of humor, even God. Caregivers may require a bit more help cultivating theirs.

Caregiving is hard, wearisome work that can really cramp a lifestyle. With these few ideas, you can inject a lot of sunshine and fresh air into a dreary situation. By doing so, the one you love benefits from a healthy caregiver - and you as the caregiver give yourself permission to live a more meaningful and joyful life.

Through humor, you can soften some of the worst blows that life delivers. And once you find laughter, no matter how painful your situation might be, you can survive it.
Bill Cosby

Gracie and Peter
Photo Courtesy: Michael Gomez

Profession

Do Lipton employees take coffee breaks?
Steven Wright

No man goes before his time unless the boss leaves early.
Groucho Marx

According to a 2009 study conducted by the National Alliance for Caregiving in collaboration with AARP, approximately "73% of family caregivers who care for someone over the age of 18 either work or have worked while providing care." With 65 million Americans serving as a volunteer caregiver for a vulnerable loved one, that percentage reflects a vast amount of today's workforce that is saddled with the extra responsibilities of caregiving. With Baby-Boomers racing into senior status, tomorrow's workforce will have to balance caring for a huge population of aging parents. The alarm bells are sounding that a large number of individuals will require volunteer caregivers, and the trend clearly reveals that more and more workers will need to juggle their professional life while caring for a loved one.

MetLife provided a 2010 study that showed American workers from every profession struggling to balance work responsibilities while serving as a caregiver. The MetLife report revealed significantly higher costs to the employer - ranging from absenteeism to health care. These costs to American businesses soar into the billions. (*The MetLife Study of Working Caregivers and Employer Health Care Costs*)

In a robust economy, those costs and challenges to employers can be absorbed or accommodated somewhat easier. In the difficult times facing today's businesses, however, caregivers must function with extra care to avoid taxing the goodwill of employers and co-workers—as well as the "bottom line."

The caregiver who daily attends the needs of the patient serves as a critical component of that patient's overall health. Although quantifying the exact value added by a caregiver can be challenging, all can agree that a gainfully employed caregiver is in the best interest of the patient. Paychecks, housing, insurance, food —the entire patient-care ecosystem for many individuals depends upon the physical, emotional, and professional health of the caregiver. Certainly not all patients have a family member or friend serving as a caregiver; and clearly not all caregivers maintain full-time employment. Yet, according to the studies, approximately 47 million American workers are serving as volunteer caregivers for an aging, disabled, or chronically ill loved one.

As someone who has faced this issue on an extreme level, I receive many requests to address this topic. My passion is to equip caregivers with easy and practical tips on not only staying employed, but also excelling in the workplace.

One of the most challenging issues I face as a caregiver for twenty-seven years is balancing work and my wife's chronic and pressing medical issues.

I recall days which started somewhat "normal," but by the time our sons' school let out, my wife was admitted into the hospital—and facing surgery. Juggling the medical crisis alone is challenging. Living up to work responsibilities, however, while somehow keeping the plates spinning of picking up children, fixing meals, and swinging by the hospital to meet with doctors—can make for some extra stressful workdays.

When the caregiver is the business owner or boss, scheduling work may be easier, but the stress of keeping the business going brings additional challenges.

Employees serving as caregivers regularly find themselves in tight work situations that often require appeasing one demand, while disappointing another. Saying "no" to a hurting family member in order to maintain work responsibilities can significantly strain an already stretched home life. Saying "no" to an employer, however, presents a new basket of problems. Caregivers often find themselves balancing on the tightrope of not presuming upon the generosity of fellow employees and supervisors, while keeping crises at bay on the home front.

Is it any wonder that many caregivers decline increased wages through promotions in order to avoid the extra responsibility that comes with workplace advancement? Sometimes, it is even easier to leave the workforce altogether. This decision affects not only the household budget, but is ultimately felt in the community (local businesses), lack of charitable giving (churches, non-profits, etc.), and even in the tax base of our national economy.

For many years, I took jobs I really did not aspire to, all for insurance and flexibility of schedule. Like many caregivers, my earning potential and advancement took hits on numerous occasions. Also like many caregivers, I learned to adapt and "figured out how to make it work." Along the journey, I discovered that although many bosses and supervisors possessed understanding, they still required good communication about the circumstances.

It was while balancing work and caregiving, that I learned the three "F's."

- Be FORTHRIGHT with the Boss
- Ask for FLEXIBILITY
- Give a FAIR day's work.

Be FORTHRIGHT with the Boss

Surprises rarely create good feelings in a workplace. Employers are likely to be more understanding and accommodating if they know up front some of the challenges that may affect work performance and/or schedules. Taking a proactive stance and letting supervisors into the loop, without disclosing too much personal information, can be a help down the road when crises occur.

Sometimes a boss can be a friend, but experience cautions me to keep the relationship limited to business if possible. Human nature being what it is, disclosing too much personal information can have some drawbacks, so caregivers need to show extra savvy to only provide that which is pertinent to the workplace.

A qualified counselor (private or through an Employee Assistance Program) can serve as a sounding board for how to approach a supervisor in order to discuss caregiving circumstances. Human Resources directors can also be a help in this matter. Counselors, therapists, and pastors can all serve as another source of wisdom and coaching in helping formulate a plan to approach a boss or supervisor.

Ask for FLEXIBILITY

The answer is always "no" until you ask. Work schedules are not the Ten Commandments. Where does it say, "Thou shalt not swap shifts?" Who says working from home on certain occasions is out of the question? The evolution of the modern workforce is astonishing. No longer do we have an industrial mindset where work only happens during certain and specific hours of the day. Many jobs cater to the global economy - and the mobile and virtual offices that define today's workplace. Granted, a nurse at a hospital or a server at a restaurant works well-structured shifts, but those and many other jobs are "tweak-able."

Give a FAIR day's work

By demonstrating to co-workers that caregivers deliver quality work without sloughing off, we can also earn many "chips" to cash in during extreme scenarios. No one wants to help lazy or entitlement-minded individuals, so by earning a reputation as an industrious and responsible employee (and we caregivers are by definition industrious and responsible people), other workers and supervisors will feel more inclined to accommodate shift changes, task reassignments, and even tardiness or leaving early.

In my years of caregiving, I developed a simple numeric plan of "**1-2-30**" to help me stay on track in all the major impact areas of caregiving. Those areas affected by caregiving are: health, emotions, lifestyle, profession, money, and endurance (they spell out HELP ME!) For the profession component, I found the following items to be easy reminders of how to shore up the "professional front" of my life and improve my standing in the workplace. Staying with the **1-2-30** system, the following ideas have provided great help to me:

1 training class per year to learn new skills

From *Power Point* to fixing a car, there are always new skills a caregiver can learn. Many companies will pay for ongoing training, computer training, and even collegiate and post-graduate work. Taking advantage of the opportunity to improve as an employee, as well as a person, is a smart move. One training class per year is doable. In order to not "bite off more than one can chew," it is wise to avoid trying to earn a doctorate or other grand achievements in one year. Keeping in mind the importance of managing expectations, taking a computer class, for example, might be a place to start. Maybe learning management skills would be a good direction for a server at a restaurant.

At lunch recently, a friend mentioned the story of a woman in his church whose husband suffered from multiple sclerosis. Working as a physical therapist, she served as the major income source for her family. Without any warning, she arrived at work one day to discover a pink-slip. Out of work with a disabled husband and two small children - well, you can imagine the fear gripping this woman.

After an unsettling and stressful time, she has since landed a new job. Although all seems to be well, there exists an opportunity to help her minimize the risk of this reoccurring. What if her pastor/church leaders approached her and said, "We know this was a scary time, and, although we can't keep this from happening again, we want to help you better insulate yourself from unemployment. If you are willing, we can help arrange childcare and even possibly underwrite your taking a class once a week or so - to become more proficient in your field."

How do you think the woman would respond? In that situation, the church is caring for the practical needs, as well as the spiritual needs of this family. It may not mean much of a financial investment on the part of the church. Maybe just coordinating childcare would be sufficient, but either way, it helps this woman develop a plan that will ultimately provide a greater sense of security for this family. Keeping this woman employed is in the best interest of the family, church, and society.

On a recent episode of 60 Minutes, I heard a major employer state, "... In today's economy, workers cannot expect to remain employed with the same skill set they started with." By improving "market value" as an employee by learning one new job-related skill set each year, the risk of unemployment reduces.

2 performance meetings per year with supervisor

While some dread an annual review with a boss, I take the opposite approach and push for even more opportunities to evaluate performance and iron out potential employment landmines. A consistent need for scheduling flexibility can increase tension among co-workers. Through regular communication with a supervisor, however, a boss can become an ally and help run interference with disgruntled colleagues. Just like visiting a physician twice a year provides an opportunity to discover potential health issues, two performance meetings per year with a supervisor can help identify potential employment issues.

Caregivers cannot afford to lose their job due to office politics, backstabbing by other employees, or any other performance issues possibly connected to caregiving responsibilities. Regular communication with an employer serves as a proactive way of keeping channels open, clearing up misunderstandings before they escalate, and demonstrating initiative and responsibility.

30 minutes DAILY away from desk/phone

The common mistake of wolfing down a sandwich at your desk, while fielding calls and working in a game of solitaire - just will not cut it for caregivers (or any worker, for that matter). Take a break.

Getting away from your desk or workplace is critical for working caregiver's peace of mind, even if it means just sitting in the car with a book and NO phone. Somewhere near the workplace a bench is waiting for a weary caregiver who needs a quiet place to collect his/her thoughts. Every employer in America offers a break during the workday, and it is imperative to workers, specifically caregiving workers, to accept those breaks in order to recharge, refocus, and rest for at least thirty minutes during each workday.

The strain of caregiving presents challenges in and of itself, but in an unstable economy, the workplace is liable to be precarious for any worker requiring greater flexibility. By incorporating such strategies as better communication and improving value to an employer, caregivers can reduce the risk of unemployment and job tension(s). With a proactive approach, today's caregivers can not only minimize the risk of unemployment, but can even position themselves for advancement.

Caring for the patient is not limited to medically related tasks. Healthy caregivers make better caregivers, and part of being a healthy caregiver for tens of millions of Americans is remaining a *successfully employed* caregiver. In doing so, those working caregivers help provide resources and stability to vulnerable loved ones who desperately needs both.

Money

Money isn't the most important thing in life,
but it's reasonably close to oxygen on the "gotta have it" scale.
Zig Ziglar

Caregiving is challenging enough, but adding money issues to the mix creates a massive strain on individuals and families. Three decades of caregiving experience leads me to believe that although they may help, I cannot permanently rely on a government program, individual, family member, or a lottery ticket to come to my rescue. *By the way, the lottery is simply a tax on people who are bad at math.* The only permanent thing in this scenario is that caregiving requires long hours, weary nights, and constant battles to stretch a dollar until it is translucent.

From a server struggling to make tips working at Cracker Barrel while caring for a sick spouse, to multi-millionaire children able to pay for full-time care for aging parents, I've encountered individuals in virtually every type of caregiving situation. Most of us fall somewhere in the middle - but lean towards the server trying to squeeze out a living.

- Caregiving families (families in which one member has a disability) have median income that are more than 15% lower than non- caregiving families. In every state and DC the poverty rate is higher among families with members with a disability than among families without. 6

- During the 2009 economic downturn, 1 in 5 family caregivers had to move into the same home with their loved ones to cut expenses.

- 47% of working caregivers indicate an increase in caregiving expenses has caused them to use up ALL or MOST of their savings.7

- The average family caregiver for someone 50 years or older spends $5,531 per year on out of pocket caregiving expenses in 2007 which was more than 10% of the median income for a family caregiver that year.8

Many financial experts share how to deal with money, get out of debt, and so forth - yet I've not heard one of them who has even remotely juggled anything like my family's three decades of surgeries, pain, constant crises, and health costs (cresting $9,000,000).

- What kind of financial impact does enduring something like this have on a family budget?

- How does this affect my ability to pay my bills, realize professional potential and earn more, prepare for retirement, have peace of mind, or tithe to my church?

- How do I keep my head above water?

- Is it possible to "get ahead?"

These questions (and more) serve as regular topics during my frequent late-night conversations with the ceiling fan.

Before launching my radio show and writing my book, *Wear Comfortable Shoes - Surviving and Thriving as a Caregiver*, I spent a great deal of time thinking about "What does 'help' look like to a caregiver?" For example, having someone bring meals to the family is helpful, but eventually someone has to learn to cook.

Likewise with money: A gift of cash in time of need is helpful. Ultimately, however, one must earn a living and effectively manage money.

The key is sustainability - and in order to manage the massive bills, extra costs, and nuances of the tax code, I have found that I need the help of trained professionals; specifically Certified Public Accountants (CPA).

I look at a CPA almost like a primary care doctor. To me, the CPA functions as the "hub" of the financial wheel of life. From mortgages to tax deductions, a CPA can serve as a guide through the financial jungle of both individual budgets and our national economy. When my heating unit needs servicing, I leave it to the professionals. When my financial "unit" needs servicing, I also call the professionals.

How many accountants does it take to change a light bulb?
Hmmmm...I'll just do a few numbers and get back to you!

I won't presume to tell anyone, particularly caregivers, how to manage their money. I can offer a few things that changed the way I view money, helped me keep a superior credit rating, and avoid bankruptcy while dealing with the massive medical bills incurred for the last several decades.

Again, using the 1-2-30 system:

1 charity to financially support

Over the years, I discovered that thinking about someone else's struggles and challenges helped put mine in perspective. Even though my wife and I founded a non-profit ourselves, we give to others that are totally unrelated to what we do at *Standing With Hope*, and also have nothing to do with the caregiving, disability, and amputation issues we daily face.

We found that by focusing on issues other than our own, it allowed us to "get outside ourselves," if only for a brief moment. At some point, everyone in life hurts, deals with problems, and generally struggles. It is mentally and emotionally unhealthy to place my individual issues at the center of the universe. Looking to make a difference in the lives of others reframes how important my *crisis du jour* really is, and in doing so offers an opportunity to look at my circumstances in a different light. Self-pity and self-importance lead to mental and emotional dysfunction, which hampers the ability to think clearly in high stress moments.

Caregivers regularly endure tense situations, so keeping a clear head and a healthy perspective becomes critical when dealing with the day-to-day stresses of caregiving. Thinking about and doing something for someone else's misery, has taught me gratitude and fostered more compassion, empathy, and understanding - which spills over to my role as caregiver. Regardless of how small the amount, contributing to the betterment of others changes perspective and expands the heart of an individual.

Keep all charitable donation receipts and give them to your CPA!

2 meetings per year with a financial advisor

Taxes, bills, and creditors, oh my! The financial matters caregivers deal with are daunting on a good day, insane on a bad one. For one person to carry all of the financial burdens of caregiving is just too much, and errors are inevitable. Having a second (or third) set of eyes helps bring organization and peace of mind to what can often be chaotic. A good CPA is a great ally. They're not perfect, and, like all professionals, some of them shine above others in their field. By and large, however, a good financial advisor can serve as a strong and important team member for caregivers.

For non-caregivers, if you see a caregiver who is struggling, try to avoid platitudes like, "You're in our hearts and prayers." Instead, ask them, "Do you have a CPA you regularly see?"

That simple question can direct the caregiver toward a healthier financial path - and can circumvent a slew of problems, help someone manage bills, stay current on taxes, learn to operate within a budget, and take advantage of tax-deductible expenses incurred in most caregiving scenarios.

For folks who can truly not afford it, I often encourage churches to provide leadership in this area. Clergy members can connect a caregiver to a CPA within the church who might be willing to provide discounted or even free accounting services. Underwriting the cost of two visits per year to a CPA through a discretionary/benevolence fund, makes a whole lot more sense than just sending a cash "mercy gift." Caregivers struggle with long-term issues - and a path towards sustainability is more helpful than just sending a "financial band-aid." People are generally eager to help and give, but it is important to identify "real help" to caregiver faced with long-term challenges.

A CPA can also refer clients out to a good financial planner. Just as a primary care doctor refers to specialists, I trust my CPA to have relationships with qualified financial planners. Sitting down with reputable financial planners, caregivers can adequately assess such things as life insurance, disability insurance, investments, and so forth. Employment may offer many of those services, but periodically revisiting these issues ensures that products and services are up to date, organized, and easily accessible in the event of a death or injury. In addition, a CPA and financial planner become critical when setting up arrangements for children with special needs. For those with elderly parents, consider underwriting a CPA to help them with their finances if they don't have one already. Since you will most likely have to take over the responsibility of their money, wouldn't it be nice to have it all neat and tidy?

How do you know when an accountant is on vacation?
He doesn't wear a tie to work and comes in after 8:30

An important tip to remember is not to flog yourself if your finances are in disarray. Every journey starts with step one. Even today, a single step in the right direction is possible. I love the truism, "You didn't get here overnight, and you won't get out of this overnight."

It's a marathon, not a sprint; pacing one's self while wearing comfortable shoes is the key.

$30 per paycheck into savings

Caregiving often means living paycheck to paycheck - on a good week. Financially treading water for as long as caregiving requires can cause even the stoutest checkbooks to grow weary, and getting ahead sometimes seems out of the question. Putting something in a savings account can sound like it asks too much while drowning in bills. Squirreling away even a little bit, however, goes a long way towards a better night's sleep.

Although some caregivers can afford to put $30,000 per month in savings, most of us do not live in that world. Pushing ourselves to put money aside, however small the amount, accomplishes several things in our journey towards living healthy lives, one of which is forcing us to regularly look at our budget and evaluate needs versus wants. In trying to deal calmly with the "expected unexpected," knowing the cost of a new tire, plumbing repair, or a shower chair is socked away can be assuring. Health Saving Accounts (HSA) are extremely helpful and advantageous, and a good CPA can also advise on establishing one.

These simple 1-2-30 steps, which cost comparatively little, allow caregivers a measure of peace of mind in order to live a little more calmly - in what often feels like a storm. People who live in the paths of hurricanes store up batteries, fresh water, and various other supplies in the event of an emergency. Caregivers face storms lasting longer than any hurricane in recorded history. The storms caregivers face, at least for that individual and family, can also be more costly and deadly. A good CPA is simply part of "storm preparation."

Anyone can implement these 1-2-30 steps today - and immediately generate positive benefits to any situation. These simple ideas can ease the craziness and stress in a caregiver's life - and represent a few of the reasons why you should "hug your CPA today!"

The Accountant's Prayer:

Lord, help me be more relaxed about insignificant details - starting tomorrow at 10.53:16 AM, Eastern Daylight Saving Time.

Financial planning is important for everyone, but it is essential when you are managing the care of another. As a caregiver you need to evaluate the long-term needs of the one you are caring for. In making this evaluation, it is important to consider financial options and resources. Including :

- Develop a plan.

- Understand medical coverage, legal responsibilities, and security.

- Find and organize all important personal and financial documents.

- Investigate long- and- short term disability insurance.

- Learn about Medicare/Medicaid and other government programs.

Consider consulting a financial professional and an elder care attorney who specialize in working with caregivers.*

*From a financial planner.

Endurance

Therefore, since we are surrounded by so great a cloud of witnesses, let us also lay aside every weight, and sin which clings so closely, and let us run with endurance the race that is set before us.
Hebrews 12:1 *English Standard Version*

The word "marathon" best describes what caregivers face, except the finish line usually involves a funeral.

The question is, "Whose funeral?"

Bluntly speaking - none of this is easy, and quite truthfully, it will in all likelihood grow increasingly difficult. Sometimes we can insulate ourselves from the financial, professional, and even physical challenges, but never from the emotional difficulties. Our hearts hurt at watching helplessly over a loved one suffering. Until enduring it themselves, others just cannot understand the sorrow, anger, despair, and frustration that washes upon caregivers as they seek to care for someone they deeply love, but who is ravaged by disease or age.

It's a burden too great, and too sad, to endure alone, and my heart breaks for those who journey through such a trial without connecting with others who see their pain. In juggling the challenges we carry, we caregivers find ourselves in what I call the trap of the three "I's."

- **Isolation**
- **Loss of Identity**
- **Loss of Independence**

Isolation

At the onset of the condition, people surround the situation with love, meals, kindness, and attention. As time progresses, relationships wax and wane, and new faces appear on the scene, but even those fade as the months drag into years, and become decades. Others may simply not know the need, or maybe can't find the words, or the situation is just too uncomfortable to "get involved."

Regardless, time filters relationships, and the caregiver is left to fend for herself without meaningful interaction outside of a bleak situation that, at best, stays the same for long stretches ...or at worst, deteriorates. As the condition progressively worsens, more individuals may appear to shore up those involved, but that can also mean a new plateau of loss is approaching.

Isolation often occurs due to logistics. Sometimes, it is just too much work, or simply unfeasible, to transport some individuals out of the house. Other times, caregivers, embarrassed about the condition of their loved one, or wishing to protect their dignity, remove themselves from the public eye.

Regardless of the reasons, caregivers, and those they look after, require positive connections with other human beings. That's why it is so important to engage in church, community, and other social networks.

Loss of Identity

Virtually everyone that sees me immediately starts the question by asking how Gracie is doing. I appreciate their concern, but I will admit it's quite meaningful when someone inquires about me.

My challenge, however, is to answer the question.

On the few times I'm asked about me, I developed a bad habit of launching into Gracie's condition. A good friend once stopped me and brought attention to that fact, and then gave me another shot at answering his question about my well-being.

In talking with other caregivers, I've noticed I'm not the only one who does this. A caregiver's identity seems to somehow get lost in the world and details of the one they care for, and it often requires a conscious effort to speak in first person (singular).

Although understandable, caregivers losing their identity leads to many other problems including co-dependency, resentment, depression, and the inability to make independent (and critical) decisions.

> When a co-dependent dies, someone else's life flashes
> in front of their eyes. --*Unknown*

Others may never quite get it, and still see only the person in the wheelchair. When the ones that do see the hurting caregiver, however, inquire about him/her, that is the perfect opportunity to implement (maybe slowly at first) sharing some real feelings. It may feel awkward the first few times, but expressing the heart, even while stammering, releases a lot of stress.

The flip-side is that so many caregivers crave attention and interaction that their neediness gets the better of them and they make people "drink from the fire hose" by dousing listeners with way too much information. Given that a truckload of emotions may tumble out to the first sincere person who asks, it's usually a good idea to breathe slowly while thinking about each word.

Sharing from the heart takes practice and trust, so a little patience is needed for a caregiver inexperienced at speaking about themselves.

> This above all: to thine own self be true.
> Hamlet Act 1: scene 3. --*Shakespeare*

Loss of Independence

Somewhere along the way, we lost the ability to just "jump and run" as a couple, and as a family. It happens.

Caregiving trumps "doing whatever you want, whenever you want," and can be quite an adjustment. Of course, an argument can be made that independence is only an illusion. For the sake of this conversation, however, I think we can all agree that caring for a sick loved one means that your own personal independence is substantially reduced.

Throughout this book, I've stated the importance of taking a break. Getting away from the responsibilities and pressures of caregiving and carving out some "me" time is critical when looking after someone for long periods of time. Along with the loss of identity, a reduction in independence leads to resentment and anger, and can eventually result in abandonment. By learning to carve out time for yourself, you are pro- longing and increasing your ability to properly care for your loved one.

Some situations are so dire, that the caregiver literally feels chained to another human being. But even in those situations, proper boundaries can still be maintained so that one person's life does not consume another.

With my wit and sense of humor, I make other people laugh, but I can't make anyone happy. They choose that for themselves. While saying and doing certain things, I can serve as a source of comfort and pleasure to others, I can also exhibit behavior that is unpleasant and harmful. But in both extremes, I am powerless to make another person happy or sad.

This understanding is important to maintaining a healthy independence from the person receiving care. Their state may be miserable and even pitiful, but how much power do any of us have to change their circumstances? We can be polite, caring, attentive, and upbeat, but they have to choose their own emotional and mental state. I've seen individuals in severe pain who exude joy and happiness, but I've also met those living with far less dire circumstances who are miserable, and seem to want to make everyone around them also feel miserable.

If Gracie is having a bad day, does it mean that I have to as well? If I am in a bad mood, does she need to join me in the grumpy cellar?

Of course not.

We can and must function as independent individuals, regardless of how crammed together we are through the "journey of suffering patient and caregiver." It's not easy, but it is possible.

The key is detaching, but with love. Sometimes I become so weary and frustrated that I want to detach with extreme prejudice. An amputation isn't required in order to detach, it's a simple unlocking. The key to unlocking is knowing the limits and boundaries. I cannot cure, fix, change, or control the terrible things she endures. The only thing I can control is my behavior.

When she wants to do something that I think is foolish, unwise, or even harmful, I can't stop her, unless I am prepared to manage every decision she makes for the rest of her life. (As if she would let me!)

A woman once shared with me that she couldn't get away from her aging father because every time she left, something bad would occur. "He falls each time I leave him with someone else!" she said, while tearing up in frustration.

"Something bad happens whether you are there or not." I told her. "You can't guarantee your presence will forever prohibit him from falling. If you've done your best to provide safeguards and to have someone there in the event of a fall or other mishaps, what more can you do?"

As we all struggle with the independence issue, these questions require top consideration:

- Will your loved one's life improve if you are out of the picture?
- Are you able to care for them when you are emotionally and physically exhausted?
- Will they be better off once you're a "husk of a human being?"

87

Looking at those questions, "seeking and maintaining" a healthy level of emotional and even physical independence becomes critical to not only the caregiver, but to the patient as well.

"Taking care of yourself is of utmost importance, even more than taking care of your loved one. If you are not healthy (mentally, physically, emotionally, spiritually) you are simply no good to your loved one, and you become a drain on yourself, as well as your loved one - all the while believing that you are helping."
- *James S. Rosenberger*, Licensed Clinical Social Worker (brother of the author)

Understanding that caregiving is a marathon, and caregivers require endurance to resist becoming isolated while maintaining their identity and independence, use the 1-2-30 system to strengthen that endurance.

1 daily contact outside of the home

While limited to just one, make an effort to reach out to at least one person who can speak encouragement to YOU. Churches across the country have wonderful programs such as Stephen Ministers who can function beautifully in this area, but you have to initiate this. It may feel awkward, even weird, at first, but you, and the person you love cannot afford for YOU to become isolated. Social media and email don't count. Face to face is the best, but not always possible, so pick up the   phone and call a friend.

2 hours per week of "Me" time

Do something for yourself. Take a long walk in the park, go to a movie or museum, play a round of golf, or go to a craft show. Do something that's for you, that you enjoy. It doesn't have to cost money. Maybe it's curling up with a good book with a sign on your door that reads, "Off- duty." Whatever you choose, it's about your physical and emotional independence. No matter how others may interpret this, you are not being selfish. Quite the opposite, you are doing what is necessary to bring your "A-Game" as a caregiver.

30 minutes per day of quiet time/devotional

You may want to read your Bible, a devotional, or just sit quietly. What- ever you choose, it is your time to be still and alone with your thoughts - and God. Take more time than thirty minutes if desired, but try not to take less. Your peace of mind won't come, until you seek peace, and that comes from learning to be still. Peace is sought, not inflicted.

"...Be still and know that I am God."
Psalm 46:10 King James Version

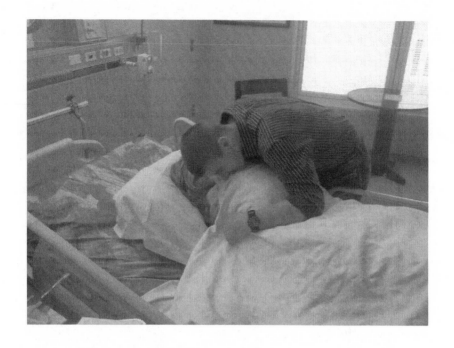

Grayson Rosenberger with his mother in the hospital

When Your Heart Is Hurting and Weary

Seeing that a Pilot steers the ship in which we sail, who will never
allow us to perish even in the midst of shipwrecks,
there is no reason why our minds should
be overwhelmed with fear and overcome with weariness.
John Calvin

In Ephesians, Paul encourages Christians to "...put on the whole armor of God." Part of that armor included "your feet shod with the Gospel of Peace."

This book is about practical tips and pointing to the only source capable of sustenance to those caring for a suffering human being. "Wear Comfortable Shoes" is not just a catchy title and a nice practical tip, it's a lifestyle of putting on something that will comfort, sustain, strengthen, and equip us. That something is the Gospel of Jesus Christ ...the good news that God made a way for us to be reconciled to Him.

As bad as the events in our life may be, the truth is, as believers, this broken, pain-filled world is as close to Hell as we will ever have to be. No sneakers or slippers I own, bring greater comfort to me than this truth.

That notwithstanding, there are still moments (often days) when my heart is so weary and my shoulders stoop from the burdens I carry. During those moments, I can't think clearly, and sometimes, I can't even see clearly.

In those bleak times, I recall these things to mind, and, with my feet "shod with the Gospel of Peace", I strengthen and encourage my weary heart, while also wearing comfortable shoes.

"...and, as shoes for your feet, having put on the readiness
given by the gospel of peace."
Ephesians 6:15 (English Standard Version)

When you heart is weary, use these numbers 1-2-30

1 Savior

There is one Savior, and I am not Him ...nor are you. Look down at your hands, if you don't see nail scars, then you are not responsible for fixing all of this. You are only responsible for your own actions and what comes out of your mouth.

One day, this Savior's plans will be clear, and all of this will be made right for those who trust in Him. That's where our faith comes in, and I cling to, and draw strength from, this promise:

And God shall wipe away all tears from their eyes; and there
shall be no more death, neither sorrow, nor crying, neither shall
there be any more pain: for the former things are passed away.
Revelation 21:4 (King James Version)

2 Hymns

There are times when no words can express the pain, frustration, fear, and sorrow caregivers have. During those moments in my life, I recall two great hymns of the faith, written by those who understood feelings like mine, but anchored themselves into a truth transcending heartache.

> Great is Thy faithfulness! Great is Thy faithfulness!
> Morning by morning new mercies I see;
> All I have needed Thy hand hath provided—
> Great is Thy faithfulness, Lord, unto me!
> © 1923. Ren. 1951 Hope Publishing Co.

It Is Well With My Soul - Horatio Spafford/Phillip Bliss

> When peace, like a river, attendeth my way,
> When sorrows like sea billows roll;
> Whatever my lot, Thou has taught me to say,
> It is well, it is well, with my soul.
>
> Though Satan should buffet, though trials should come,
> Let this blest assurance control,
> That Christ has regarded my helpless estate,
> And hath shed His own blood for my soul.
>
> My sin, oh, the bliss of this glorious thought!
> My sin, not in part but the whole,
> Is nailed to the cross, and I bear it no more,
> Praise the Lord, praise the Lord, O my soul!
> And Lord, haste the day when my faith shall be sight,
> The clouds be rolled back as a scroll;
> The trump shall resound, and the Lord shall descend,
> Even so, it is well with my soul.

30 Words

For those really bad moments, when hymns and practical tips fly out of my mind, I concentrate on just thirty words. These words are part of Psalm 23, which has sustained and comforted untold billions of hurting hearts.

"..Yea, though I walk
through the valley of the shadow of death,
I will fear no evil for thou art with me.
Thy rod and Thy staff, they comfort me."
- *Psalm 23:4* (King James Version)

Tips for Caregivers

1-2-30 Plan for Caregivers

Health
> 1 flu shot
> 2 well visits
> 30 Minutes of daily exercises

Emotions
> 1 counseling session per month
> 2 support groups
> 30 days in church per year

Lifestyle
> 1 thing per week that YOU like to do
> 2 weeks vacation from caregiving per year
> 30 minutes of laughter ...daily

Profession
> 1 training class per year to learn a new skill
> 2 performance meeting with supervisor each year
> 30 minutes daily away from desk/phone

Money
> 1 charity you can financially support
> 2 meetings per year with a financial advisor
> $30 per paycheck into savings/investment

Endurance
> 1 daily contact with positive/loving friends or family members
> 2 hours per week of "Me time"
> 30 minutes daily devotional/quiet time.

For Weary Hearts
> 1 Savior
> 2 Hymns (*Great is Thy Faithfulness/It Is Well With My Soul*)
> 30 Words: *Yea, though I walk through the valley of the shadow of death, I will fear no evil for thou art with me. Thy rod and Thy staff, they comfort me.*

The following section contains different articles from various viewpoints including:

- For Caregivers of Spouses
- Caring For an Elderly Parent
- For Caregivers Who Are Parents
- From a Teenager Caring for a Sibling
- From a Caregiving Wife, Daughter, and Mother
- Tips For Dealing with Annual Deductibles
- A Long Distance Caregiver
- For a Non-Caregiver
- Tips from a Case Manager

For Caregivers of Spouses

Peter W. Rosenberger

Raising a family and keeping love alive in a marriage with a spouse who is constantly sick or in severe pain is an extreme challenge; one with many casualties. The divorce rate in couples with a disability in the family hovers around 90% and relationships with a disability or chronic medical condition face significant pressures on the love holding the marriage together. In my many years of caregiving I've observed and am learning four particular concepts that help allow love to transcend the harsh realities of living with someone who is sick and hurting —realities that can easily destroy a love.

1. Separate the person from the pain

How do you keep love and passion thriving in a chronic medical catastrophe where the suffering is not limited to a short-term illness or injury?

Different from Alzheimer's or dementia, marriages impacted by one spouse living with a broken or diseased body while retaining complete cognitive awareness encounter a different set of emotional trials for the marriage. The challenge for the healthy spouse is to maneuver through the minefield of medical issues, attending to each of them, but never losing sight of the suffering person's heart. Taking care of the body does not always equate to caring for the heart.

The challenge for the sick or injured spouse, even from a wheelchair or while in severe chronic pain, is to recognize that matters of the heart, though often less demanding , are just as important (if not more so) as the needs of the body.

2. Live while hurting

It is appropriate to acknowledge our hurts, but, after nearly three decades of living with someone who daily suffers from severe chronic pain, I have witnessed the difference between "living with pain" versus "living while in pain." My wife didn't have to go to Africa and launch a prosthetic limb ministry. She could have easily chosen to focus on herself and her own challenges. She purposed, however, to give out of her lack—and in doing so, she continues to touch a great many lives even though she can no longer travel. She saw something worthwhile that did not reduce her pain, but rather transcended it. The lesson I learned from this is that is possible and rewarding to live a full and rich life while in pain.

We don't have to wait until we "feel good" before we participate and our successful in life. I remember a special night in Madison Square Garden right after President George W. Bush gave his acceptance speech for the nomination in 2004. Invited to be on the platform behind the President following Gracie's performance at the convention two nights prior, we had to be in place on the stage early in the evening. For several hours we sat there, while my wife's pain levels escalated. She knew she would be uncomfortable, and she knew it would be a long night, but we lived in the moment together, and after the President left, we danced together among the fallen balloons and confetti while country singer Lee Ann Womack stood just feet away singing her hit song, "I Hope You Dance."

Gracie did opt to forgo wearing dress shoes in order to be a bit more comfortable. You can still see us in pictures sitting just behind the President's left shoulder. Gracie's robotic-looking legs are in plain view with her bright white sneakers—which I think is hilarious! If Gracie and the President of the United States didn't mind, no one else should!

3. Love while hurting

Everyone hurts at some point; even supermodels and professional athletes suffer physically at times. Using sickness or feeling bad as an excuse to disconnect from the needs of close relationships sets a horrible and destructive precedent that seems to say, "I can be focused only on me whenever I feel bad."

Experience teaches me that life-changing and transcending love abounds when we choose to turn our eyes to others—particularly (and peculiarly) while carrying great burdens ourselves.

We cannot escape the relentless difficulties in this life;

we do however, have the opportunity to embrace each other, even while in pain, and discover love ...and romance, are not dependent on external circumstances, but instead reside solely in the heart. As the wonderful Rodgers and Hart song stated so well:

> My romance doesn't have to have a moon in the sky
> My romance doesn't need a blue lagoon standing by;
> No month of May, no twinkling stars,
> No hide away, no soft guitars.
>
> My romance doesn't need a castle rising in Spain,
> Nor a dance to a constantly surprising refrain.
> Wide awake,
> I can make my most fantastic dreams come true.
> My romance doesn't need a thing but you.

4. See the heart, not "the chart"

For caregivers I offer this advice: if the love of your life struggles with chronic disease or injury, take a moment to see beyond the medical chart, the broken body and the pain-filled eyes...and connect to the heart of the extraordinary person who captured your heart. Due to medical circumstances, it may be one-sided, but that's okay.

As a caregiving spouse, I am the only person on this planet not connected by blood or money who has volunteered to care for my wife in this manner. That distinction is important and speaks to the core motivation I have for my wife: I chose her. The reasons I chose her are important and are worthy of celebrating. Even if I have to buy my own Valentine's Day card—that is still a beautiful way to honor the relationship.

And for those suffering who are able to do so—look deeply into the eyes of the weary soul who looks after you, quietly hold hands and bask in the love you both share; a love that is defying the odds.

Caring For an Elderly Parent

Nancy James

My mother had been having several medical problems the last three years of her life. My dad died in September of 2006 and she then decided to move in with my youngest sister, Theresa. Theresa has had health issues all her life. She was, and still is, a very brittle diabetic (now waiting for a kidney and pancreas transplant), and there were times that her sugars would drop and she would collapse. Being alone for her was not a good option so this seemed to be a good solution for Mom to live with her.

There were several times my sisters and I would take our Mom to one of her doctors because she complained that there was pain in her leg, and yet every time they said it was just old age. Looking back I know what it was – it was the hidden cancer we didn't know was there.

My mom suffered from macular degeneration, and her eye-sight grew worse. This became more and more of a frustration for her, especially after losing her ability to drive.

102

Now she had to depend on others to take her to the doctors, shopping , etc. Mom was one independent lady, and she terribly resented the loss of freedom. She had numerous medications, and, due to her poor eyesight, we had to come up with a way for her to see the right bottles. Marking them with colored tape so she could see the color difference, we also made a chart for ourselves on her doses, in order to help her take the right pills.

We tried a lot of different things to keep her life as normal as possible. The last good Christmas she had, my husband and I bought her one of those huge remote controls for her TV, and I also went online and found a place where I could purchase extra large Scrabble letters, so she could continue to play the game she loved so much.

Even with all the extra efforts, we all noticed that things kept growing worse, and her frustration was showing.

My oldest daughter, Chris (Mom's first grandchild), was always close to my mother. After she moved to Raleigh, NC, she really wanted grand mom to see her new house, so, in August 2010, Chris went to New Jersey to pick up my Mom, and take her to Raleigh for a week. Mom enjoyed the visit, and even went to church with Chris and Jim. Their pastor, Pastor Dave Sims took the opportunity to visit at their house and spend time with Mom and speak to her about trusting Christ. Mom really liked him and made a true friend who, in subsequent weeks, would call Mom, just to see how she was doing. Growing up Catholic, Mom felt strangely close to this protestant preacher, who pastored a church she didn't even attend.

Chris drove up with Mom to my house in Virginia for a visit so she could see the rest of the great grandchildren. We had a marvelous time and Mom and I enjoyed a few early morning cups of coffee together sharing and laughing and just enjoying our time together. I drove her home after a week and all was well.

My sister, Theresa, had an episode where her sugars dropped and wound up in the hospital, so I thought it best for me to go and stay with Mom while Theresa was in the hospital so I could help Mom with her medications, etc. During this time Mom was having difficulty with getting rides from people who volunteered at the church Mom attended. Their seemingly cavalier attitude frustrated Mom, and caused her a great deal of sadness. At getting out of the house for a quick bike ride, I returned home to find Mom sitting sadly on the couch following a phone call. Asking her who called, she started crying. She said it was Pastor Dave, and, through tears, asked, "Why does he care so much about me when my own church won't help me?" Pastor Dave's kindness and caring turned Mom around. Through this, God gave me an opportunity to share Christ with Mom again as I had done many times over the years, but this time I had her heart, as well as her ears. Going through the motions at Mass for so long, Mom didn't understand a deeper relationship with Christ. The kindness of another minister opened her heart to the great awareness that Christ knew her name, her need of salvation, and desired to be intimately involved in her life.

While there we went to the doctor again and he gave her some medication that threw her for a loop. She could hardly get out of bed in the morning; she just looked like a rag doll to me. I had to help her get herself up from a chair or from bed. Sharing all this with not only Theresa, but my other two sisters, Maggie and Joan, we started developing a plan of care. My husband and I had purchased a house with a good size bedroom and private bath on the main floor, in anticipation of Mom's needs. My sisters and I talked about it, and since I had the facility and the opportunity to do this, they all agreed that it would be best for Mom to have someone around full time.

Mom was not so cooperative after arriving in our home in Virginia, and, after extensive research, we discovered her medication affected her adversely. She became hostile and mean. She was fine one minute, and then the next it was like a Jekyll and Hyde. She was even nasty to her little grandson. It just wasn't the Mom I knew and loved. Mom made up her mind that she was going to go back to New Jersey. She was going to take a bus or a train, and just go. She actually got up and left my house and walked about a mile and a half away – my daughters were out searching for her while I stayed with the kids. When she got back to the house, she sat in a chair in her bedroom and would not speak to me. I didn't realize at the time how the medication she was on was altering her mind, and in my frustration I became angry. I couldn't understand why she was acting this way. When I challenged her on her treatment of my grandson, she became more defensive. She insisted she wanted to go home and just glared at me. I think my sensitive nature became so hurt that I lashed out and told her if she wanted to go home then pack your bags and we will take you home. She would not talk to me, or anyone else. It was a stalemate.

Mom would not talk to me and did not want to be around me. Even my attempts to offer a drink or food resulted in her glaring at me; she simply refused to talk to me. Given the stress, we made the decision to take her to my sister's home for a while. I remember Mom sitting on my staircase as my husband, Bill, loaded her things into our car. I tried to put a sweater around her shoulders – she threw it down and yelled at me and said "Leave me alone!" She would not kiss me or even say goodbye – all I got was the glare - that hurtful, I hate you glare.

The next three weeks were torture. My sisters shared with me that Mom did not want to talk to me or have anything to do with me. How could something that I meant for good, turn out so bad? I was devastated. Although calling my sisters regularly to find out about Mom, they sadly shared with me that Mom wasn't interested in connecting with me at all.

As September rolled around, I remembered that one of the days in the month is Grand Parents Day, so I took that as an opportunity to reach out to Mom again, and, amazingly, she talked to me as if nothing had happened. That was my first wasted set of three weeks during the last six months of my Mom's life.

Gratefully, her doctor changed her medication, and Mom improved. She was more herself, and even went to my sister's retirement party, as well as the birthday party of an old friend in Philadelphia. She had a great time, and even was dancing around at the age of 88 at the party. It looked like she was the Mom we all knew and loved.

Then disaster struck on October 20th when Mom fell in the bath- room and broke the femur bone in her right leg. As she was rushed to the hospital and surgery, I left Virginia to be with her. Arriving at the hospital, I was stunned to see her in good spirits, and even took pictures of her smiling so I could send them to all the relatives. By the end of the week, her doctors had decided to send her to a local rehab center for physical therapy in order to walk again. We got her settled in there on the following Saturday. Her 89th birthday was the next week so I had taken up her birthday presents and we had a good time opening them together. She was to start her physical therapy on Monday and all looked good. Feeling she was safe and stable, and would be up and around in the weeks to come, I returned home.

Physical therapy on Monday, however, turned out to be a

harbinger. With severe pain in her leg, an MRI was ordered to determine the cause. The diagnosis was not good. She had cancer on her spine and bowel. The pain she complained about the last three years was finally explained.

After an effort at some radiation, the decision was made to send her home and coordinate with hospice care. Embarrassingly ignorant about such things, I knew sick people had help in their homes some- times, but I never realized that hospice meant "last." My mind finally grasped it, they sent my Mom home to die.

The hospice group came in and set up my Mom's bedroom with a hospital bed and all the necessary equipment for her care. The hospice nurses were thoughtful and respectful of all of us and explained things to us. I think I still had it in my head that Mom was going to get well and walk again. I was not prepared for the end of her life.

I traveled back and forth several times from Virginia to New Jersey to stay a week at a time with my Mom and then I left to come home for Christmas in a very severe snow storm. It was so bad that I almost didn't make it home. The entire East Coast was slammed. I left on December 20 so I could get back in enough time to finish my Christmas shopping, in order to be with my kids and grand kids for Christmas. For nearly three weeks, I would call every day, and all seemed to go okay. I asked my sisters to promise to tell me when they thought I should come up again. The winter was horrible. It was hard to decide when to go up.

Then the third week of January, Maggie called me and said things were changing and that I might want to get up there. I left the next day and stayed till the end.

God provided the most precious woman caretaker from hospice named Faustina. She was from Uganda, and loved the Lord. She would sing hymns or hum while she worked on my Mom's needs. I was able to help her change the linens on the bed when necessary – lifting Mom up and washing her and changing her diapers. Taking care of your mother this way is a very humbling experience. You realize this is the woman who bore you, raised you and loved you and now it is your turn to give back. As hard as it was emotionally sometimes to do things, it also was a pleasure to do what needed to be done. Sometimes we would watch TV – Mom couldn't see, but she could hear it. I purchased some old movies that I could play on her DVD player, and we really enjoyed one of her favorites, "White Christmas."

During the weeks that followed Mom continued to go downhill, but up until the last couple of days there was always that spark in her eyes. I remember the last full day of her life. She couldn't eat anymore, she could barely take a few drops of water, and to me the cruelty of it was that they were letting her die – dehydrate the life out of her. That's what it seemed like to me. It was so difficult to see her like this – now almost completely helpless.

Thankfully, over the course of the last few weeks God provided opportunities for me to be alone with Mom, and pray with her and for her. I was living at the house at that time, so I was able to just sit and talk about life and God and the kids -anything that came to mind. Mom loved music, so I took my computer in her room, placed it on her dining table and played hymns for her. Faustina would go in and start singing herself and I joined her on a couple of occasions. One of the songs that I found was "It is Well With My Soul." That song energized me and gave me strength and hope that Mom finally "got it." That last day, as my sisters and I, along with her best friend, Diana, were standing around her bed, Mom looked straight at me with her still bright and beautiful blue eyes. Speaking to her directly, I asked her if she understand God's plan of salvation, and she assured me that she did. I honestly think with all my heart that she put it all together – all those years of trying to explain what accepting Jesus Christ as personal Savior meant and all those prayers, I finally looked at her with total peace. I was confident that she accepted Christ's sacrifice on the cross on behalf of her sins, her loss state, and her desperate need of a Savior.

She passed this life around 2:00 a.m. on February 4th. Exactly four months to the day of her coming home to hospice care. We called hospice, they examined her body, declared her dead, and then the funeral home came to take her body away. My other two sisters came to the house, and, after a good cry, started to make plans for Mom's funeral. At the service, we sang, "It Is Well With My Soul." A song that mom didn't learn until nearly the end of her life, it carried her from this life to the next, and it still carries me.

I believe there is nothing harder and yet more rewarding than caring for a sick parent. It is a lonely thing to do, particularly when the parent can no longer communicate. In the end, however, it is so worth it. I have so many great memories of Mom. Even the memories of her sickness and her death hold great meaning and peace to me, because she knew how much I loved her, and she knew I was there for her.

My own family graciously gave me blessing and understanding, knowing that I had to sacrifice time with them in order to be back and forth with Mom. The sacrifice wasn't merely physically, but emotionally, financially, and even spiritually--as I struggled to process all the dynamics of losing my mother over a long period of time.

I no longer have my Mom here with me, but I know because of what me and my sisters did to make the end for her the best it could be that we all have peace and joy and contentment that we did the best we could do for our mother.

Author's note: Nancy was responsible for signing Gracie and I to Liberty University Press for her book. Nancy was struggling to keep up with reading manuscripts while dealing with the events she mentioned in this article. My first conversation with Nancy was about her mother.

For Caregivers Who Are Parents

Richard and Kim Rosenberger, my older brother and sister-in-law, have a special needs child named Kelsey. She is a delight and handful …all at the same time. Born with Cerebral Palsy and cognitive impairment, Kelsey changed Richard and Kim's lives the moment she arrived. Her older brother, Luke, and her younger brother, Heath, have also learned to experience life as caregivers for their sister, and the whole family serves as an amazing model of love, support, and innovation.

I love the statement, "it's not a lack of resources, but rather a lack of resourcefulness that causes most problems."

Richard, Kim, and their family continue to show amazing resourcefulness in loving this precious child. Here are a few tips they shared with me as parents of a special needs child for nearly 25 years.

Listen to Peter's Interview with Kim on His Radio Show
www.standingwithhope.com/caregivers

- Always keep your sense of humor.

- Never second-guess a decision you made in the moment, with the information on hand. You did what you considered was in the best interest of your child.

- Avoid a guilt trip after learning from hindsight that

your decision wasn't the best choice.

- Your child is unique and special, there isn't another person on earth who has walked in your shoes. When others give you advice, smile, thank them and make the best decision based on how you know your child and your family.

- Don't tag team parent too much. Make sure you are doing some- thing for yourself and alone with your spouse. Your children will do much better if the parents are functioning together.

- The advice we are given by the doctor when our daughter was diagnosed and we asked what we could do for her, "Take her home and love her." Pretty simple.

- Acknowledge that because of their handicap, you probably won't have them as long as your other children so make the most of the time you have.

- As much as possible, don't make the world revolve around your handicap. Work the handicap into your world.

- Don't hide out or hibernate at home. Take them with you into the world. Get out and enjoy life with your family.

- Encourage interaction with other individuals and

families. The people you meet will be much better after meeting your child. Other children grow up to be better, more tolerant adults if they are inter- acting with you and your child.

- Let your child experience new things. Get them outside often.

- Let them connect with a pet.

- Find a church and get involved.

- Enjoy life with your child!

From a Teenager Caring for a Sibling

My nephew, Heath Rosenberger (17), offers this perspective from a young man caring for his sister, Kelsey.

Dealing with a handicapped sister, both physically and mentally, is hard enough; but bringing that burden with you into school is much more difficult. As a middle and high school student, a day hasn't gone by without hearing the word "retarded." To someone that looks different, he's termed as having "the downs." (In reference to down's syndrome) Of all the bullying that goes around in schools, handicapped people take the most heat. Whether they are laughing at the special education students walking in the hall, or calling their best friend "retarded," the attacks are never ending. Having a sister with both physical and cognitive disabilities opens your eyes; it gives a whole new perspective. No one that you ever see makes fun of your sibling, so you don't feel as bad...at first. As time progresses that apathy changes to sympathy.

When I see those special education students at school, I

go out of my way to say hi to them or give them a high-five. Why? Because I know, they're still people and people need socialization. When most people see these "different" kids, they don't associate them as me and you. I didn't. I had a severely mentally retarded sister who I saw as a person, of course. But I didn't recognize those other students, which were much better off than my sister, as normal people needing friends. It took maturing for me to realize that all these kids, just like my sister, want a friend. As a sibling of a handicapped brother or sister, we never overlook them, yet, we completely ignore the other kids. We, more than anyone else, have the ability to connect with the other kids, but we choose not to. But I encourage you, take the chance. Go give that kid that's just like your sibling a high-five, and see how much it changes your view of your sibling !

Talking about your sibling publicly definitely isn't easy. We don't want to do it because we know they will just ask those questions that we don't like to answer. We know those people will always say, "Oh, I'm so sorry." I used to reply, "Oh, it's okay," so that the conversation would change subjects as quickly as possible. But why not take this as a chance to share your testimony? Why not take this as a chance to share your faith? Now whenever someone tells me how sorry they are, I like to ask "Why?" Why are they sorry? I'm not sorry. Ask anyone I know; I'm proud to have her as my sister. Where will it get you running from it? You love your sibling , but not enough to talk about her to people? This is a door! You have a testimony whether you realize it or not! Tell them about your struggles, those nights that you didn't sleep because you were crying and wondering why they are like that, those youth camps that you prayed and were so mad at God for making your sibling like that. See, that's the only way we can overcome this.

Open up.

Open up to your parents. Open up to your youth pastor. Don't be afraid to open up.

We all have heard the saying, "God has a reason for everything," but we don't realize the truth in it. God has put your sibling in your life. Use his purpose. Trust me, people's jaws will drop. This is a door for you to show how you reacted. You could've turned from God, hating him for what he's done to you and your family and your sibling. Or you can thank God and trust him. Thank him for opening your eyes to others, to love like he has loved us. Trust him when you don't know the answers, because trust me, you won't. You don't know what that person you tell your sibling about is going through, and it could just perfectly be God's timing. Explain to them why you're not sorry your sibling is that way, because God doesn't make mistakes, and because we were all, even your sibling, created in God's "Perfect" image.

Listen to Peter's Interview with Heath on His Radio Show
www.standingwithhope.com/caregivers

Wear Comfortable Shoes

From A Caregiving Wife, Daughter, and Mother

By Alice Ball Breuer
Speaker and Author of "Beyond the Dark Bayou"
www.survivingtrials.com

Why me Lord?

What am I going to do? Am I going to be OK?

These are the first questions that come to mind when a tragedy strikes; and that is normal.

Allow yourself time to think through these questions, but don't be consumed by fear and stress. Find out how you need to take care of your loved one, there are many organizations and groups that will be willing to help in any way they can; seek out the best.

Educate yourself about your patient's problem and get involved in their healthcare; for example, find the best doctor (the one who diagnosed the problem may not be the one to treat it); check out all the medications your patient is to take (get to know your pharmacist); find out what foods and exercises are best for your patient; and find ways to promote your patient's independence. Be the best patient advocate you can be.

There are many levels of caregiving. If the patient

requires 20 hours per week, almost anyone can manage that. If a patient requires several hours per day, seek help. I have found it is better to give up material things to pay for a caregiver and keep your health and sanity. There are some organizations that will help with respite care.

- Give your patient as much independence and responsibility as possible, this will increase their self-esteem.
- Do not make your patient co-dependent.
- Do not try to keep your patient from struggling, there is power in struggling that can lead to total dependence on God.

Fear of what will happen between diagnosis and death is a real emotion. Feel that emotion with your patient (cry, be angry, allow self-pity for a moment), accept your challenge (choose to be better instead of bitter), then release your emotion (give yourself time by dwelling on God's Word), and then return to being with your patient. Remember your patient will want to go on living instead of dying , so help your patient live.

When we fit in with God's plan, we will be OK, it's the fight with God that gets us into trouble with fear, depression and the list never ends. Remember, only by the Grace of God, you could be the patient; so "caregive as you would like for someone to caregive for you."

It is equally important to take care of yourself as it is to take care of your patient, because when you are not up to par, neither is your ability to take care of your patient. I had to learn to be a receiver and allow others to help me. The Bible says it is more blessed to give than to receive, I always had to be the giver; however, God taught me someone has to be the receiver. So allow yourself to be the receiver and when your challenge has passed, you can return to being the giver.

Pay attention to the warning signs listed below which can be problems for caregivers:

- Sleeping problems - too much or too little.
- Easily irritated or angered.
- Change in eating habits - weight gain or loss.
- Physical problems - headaches, stomach aches or other physical problems.
- Loss of interest in activities you used to enjoy.
- Loss of energy.
- Find out about the caregiving resources available to you.
- Look for faith-based groups for support and help.
- Ask for help and receive it.
- Join a support group for caregivers in your same situation.
- See your doctor for a checkup and address any issues you may have.
- Get enough sleep and rest.
- Eat a healthy diet – fruits, vegetables, fish, chicken, whole grains, foods low in saturated fats, and no trans fats.

- Take a multivitamin (and other vitamins if you feel you need them.) Stress uses vitamins in your body, and the B-50 balanced complex has worked for me to control stress.
- Exercise is essential, find the time for at least 20 minutes per day, walking works for me.
- Prioritize, make lists and establish a daily routine; however, adjust your agenda if needed.
- Stay in touch with family and friends, being social can help reduce stress.
- Live each day to the fullest and don't worry about tomorrow.

As a caretaker, I have learned the following:
- Life is a mystery to be lived, and not a problem to be solved.
- To caregive as I would like someone to caregive for me.
- I will be OK, because if God brings me to it, He will see me through it.

Remember, God is your source of joy and strength. Every morning, get up and say out loud, "I can do all things through Christ who strengthens me." *Philippians 4:13* New King James Version

Everyone is on a journey of life, strive to enjoy yours.

Listen to Peter's Interview with Alice on His Radio Show
www.standingwithhope.com/caregivers

Tips for Dealing with Annual Deductibles

Peter W. Rosenberger

Each January, in addition to bills from Christmas, those pesky medical insurance deductibles begin anew; adding a little more excitement to the stack of things screaming at a checkbook still deflated from holiday expenses. Now deductibles aren't a problem for everyone, but when a household member has chronic or permanent medical issues, the roll- over at the first of the year can be a bit challenging.

In order to keep my head above water and not pay massive premiums every month, I purposely set my wife's deductible to the highest amount allowed, but that means I have to scrape together a goodly sum before her insurance company pays even one dime. In addition, a co-pay adds (at least) another $1,000 before her bills are covered at one hundred percent (if it is in-network). With a case like my wife's that has included seventy-plus operations, it usually means we're out of pocket thousands of dollars before March (often in January!).

After dealing with this for more than twenty-five years, I have learned a few tips on handling these kinds of expenses each year; tips that may be helpful to others struggling with long-term medical issues - and those who already have health insurance. For those who do not have health insurance, that's a longer conversation. It appears that individuals without policies will have to sign on with the new Affordable Health Care Plan (OBAMACARE), or pay a fine. I'm not a fan, but I can't fight that battle.

For the record, I am a bit leery of politicians when it comes to health care. I know more about health care than most of the elected officials in Washington, and I don't usually trust people who pass legislation down party lines - that affects 300 million people. Politicians pay a lot of money to get their job, and spend a lot of other people's money to keep those jobs. That in itself makes me feel queasy when listening to them fawn to cameras about how much they care about others.

Back to tips about deductibles.

First, although billing offices for doctors and hospitals state that payment is due upon service, have them file it with your insurance company first …and ask them to bill you whatever the insurance company doesn't pay. Your insurance company may have a preferred provider contract with your doctor or hospital, so the rates could change significantly - even for out of pocket charges. If you are dealing with a long-term illness or disability, you will have chronic bills to match your chronic condition, so don't be in a hurry to write checks. Most providers would rather you owe them, instead of needing to send you a check for an overpayment. Let the dust settle from the insurance company, and then evaluate   what you owe.

Second, read the bills thoroughly to ensure the charges and dates of service are legitimate. Most doctors, labs, and hospitals use good computer systems, but human beings still enter the data. Serving as my wife's caregiver for a couple of decades, I learned a long time ago to check the statements. To date, her medical bills are approaching $9 million, and, along the way, I have discovered numerous billing mistakes. Keep files for every provider (preferably scanned and indexed) and double- check the explanation of benefits (EOB) relating to every bill issued by providers.

Third, make a point to get to know the billing office for all the providers you use. My wife has five key physicians, two hospitals, two pharmacists, and a prosthetist she regularly visits. Each of these providers not only knows us well, but their billing offices are also familiar with her case. Through many conversations with them, I have clearly communicated that she is a "regular" and will be requiring their services …for the long haul. It may seem unnecessary to tell a provider that a patient with a permanent disability will be a "regular," but just like everyone else, doctors and hospital staff sometimes miss the obvious.

A fourth item to keep in mind is that your providers' office will work with you on the charges you are responsible to pay. Of the high deductible/co-pay that I am responsible for every year, it is usually split between three or four providers. Home Depot and Lowes will offer interest-free specials on a microwave oven, so don't feel nervous or weird about discussing a no-interest payment arrangement with your medical providers. Most all of them do it anyway, but in the event that you have a provider that wants to charge you interest - tell them "no," and get another provider. After working with more than fifty doctors and twelve hospitals, I am yet to meet a provider who won't work with me on some type of payment plan; sometimes as little as $15 a month.

Should a billing office employee treat you disrespectfully while you are sincerely attempting to arrange a payment plan, report them immediately to their supervisor, or even to the provider. Never forget that, although a long-term illness or disability is unpleasant and difficult, your condition is profit center for hospitals, doctors, and pharmaceutical companies, and you help keep them in business. By even carrying health insurance, you have already demonstrated a high level of responsibility, and you are someone they can work with regarding payment plans. Never feel embarrassed, ashamed, or even the least self-conscious about asking to spread a deductible and co-pay over a couple of months or even a year.

Lastly, the first of every year is a good time to lay out a plan of care. Sit down with your doctor and ask them pointedly about specific goals for the year. As someone with long-term issues, your case is more complicated than a teenager who breaks an arm while playing sports. Regular discussions laying out key objectives are an important part of effectively managing a chronic illness and disability. Wound care, durable medical equipment (wheelchairs, adaptive devices, etc.), pain management, drug interactions, emotional well-being, and many other items need to be constantly evaluated and addressed. Take a list of items to each doctor visit, and be sure to update your list regularly.

No matter how professional or caring your doctor is, no one will ever care more about your condition than you do. It is important for you (or your caregiver) to demonstrate leadership to all the individuals working on "your team." Regardless of what so-called "experts" say, America's health care system is not complicated, but it can be intimidating. A little common sense, personal responsibility, and assertiveness will solve a great many of the headaches that not only arrive each January with new deductibles, but will also help with other issues that arise throughout the year.

Listen to Peter's podcast of this topic from his radio show
www.standingwithhope.com/caregivers

A Long Distance Caregiver
Our longtime friend, Bonnie Harris Moore,
offers her experience in caring for her mother from a distance.

I took care of my mom for a couple of years traveling 150 miles each way for every couple of weeks for a couple of years. It included staying in the hospital with her, moving her into assisted living , having a yard sale, selling her house myself, and then moving her to the transitional nursing wing. She had middle-stage Alzheimer's, congestive heart failure, and was an insulin-dependent diabetic.

My mom wanted to remain in the city where she grew up, met my dad, married, lived, and had many friends and family members around. However, for a time, I was the daughter with the flexibility to travel, to take her to the doctors and myriad appointments, and take care of the frequent financial and legal issues—including wrangling with the Veterans Affairs Administration to get nursing help for survivors of once-active duty servicemen. I had to drive a couple of hundred miles, stay a couple of nights, and then drive back. There was my schedule to work around, as well as planning and scheduling her appointments so as much was accomplished as possible with each visit.

One of the smartest things my sister and I did was to get co-power of attorney for mom. This allowed us to talk to doctors, hospitals, government agencies, banks, etc., without her input. We always made sure she was in the loop—when she was still able to understand these things— but being able to manage things from afar and not need Mom's input for mundane decisions made our lives easier. I also became her social security representative payee which was quite a process. First, Mom had to be declared incompetent. Since she could not remember how to balance her checkbook, her family doctor wrote a prescription stating that this was the case. He had known Mom and us for many years and knew this was the best thing for her. He also knew we girls would do our best to make sure she was well cared for.

These practical issues were the easy, though time-consuming, part of long-distance caregiving. I'm a task-oriented, organized person, so legal and financial matters are easy for me. The difficult part was dealing with the push and pull of feelings: I should be doing this, I should be doing more versus I want to do something else than this, I resent doing this. Mom and I laughed about calling my visits the tornado visits. I would rush in, get everything accomplished, and then rush out. I had to learn to occasionally take time for her, and not just what needed to be checked off the list. That was always the challenge—especially as her mental state deteriorated—and the time involved in just hanging out and making that connection increased. An example was the day we were driving back to her assisted living apartment after the third doctor's appointment in two days. We passed a favorite ice cream store and she wanted a milkshake. This is my diabetic mom, you know, but there was this little Holy Spirit nudge of "this is an important thing to her right now." So we went in, indulged ourselves, and had a great visit while we finished our ice cream. It was definitely the right thing to do and not just rushing through the time. I did, however, warn the nurses that her blood sugar might be a bit high and not to be alarmed.

My own feelings of guilt and not doing enough would swing back and forth between questions of "Am I doing what I can do?" "Am I making sure she has the best care possible?" "Are her needs being met?" and "Is she being spoiled a little, in a good way?" Mom loved decorating her apartment with the appropriate seasonal wreath and flowers, as well as wearing shirts with those seasonal appliqués. I always found time to find new ones to surprise her and a new decoration or two for the appropriate holiday. It was worth it because people came into her apartment to see her newest decorations, oooh-ing and ahh-ing over them. It was a way to help her interact with others as well. She would brag to me about all the people who liked the latest look and what they said. It was a small thing that made her feel special.

There is a lot to think about and take care of, so it is easy to forget that there is a person in there, who is not their disease, who has a personality not connected to doctors, blood work, and medicines. They can't always communicate what they are feeling or thinking, but that doesn't mean they aren't thinking and feeling.

An example of Mom wanting this kind of attention was the increased number of health issues she developed when we visited her family doctor, someone she had a patient relationship with for a long time and whom she adored. As she went over her long, and now new, list of complaints, the doctor would look at me, raise an eyebrow as if to say: "Is this for real?" and I would comment, "I didn't know that was bothering you, Mom." It was our way of communicating that this might be something that needed attention or just something that was "for that day." Then he knew where to begin his diagnosis. He always treated her with such care and concern that she felt better before we left. That was all she was really looking for sometimes, care and concern.

When so many people in your life are dealing with the specifics of your body—getting you to the bathroom, changing your sheets, getting you dressed, getting you to the dining room, getting you to the doctor— taking the time to express care and concern for them as a person often is pushed aside. The person becomes a Need instead of a Person who has needs. It is easy to forget their mental, spiritual, and non-medical physical needs as well: touching them, praying with them, asking personal questions, having a conversation that reassures them that they are still important, valued, and needed in this world.

Mom is now with the Lord and with Dad, her beloved husband of 58 years. It's been almost a year and I still find myself thinking I need to call and touch base with her at 5 PM every day, like I used to. I still think about buying seasonal shirts or wreaths for her, then remember I don't need to. Even though Mom's gone, my caregiving has not stopped. That is probably a good thing, because my care for her as my mother has not stopped either.

For a Non-Caregiver

Peter W. Rosenberger

During the Thanksgiving and Christmas holidays, stories surface about the holidays being difficult for a great number of people struggling with illness or disability. Reporters often pause to spotlight extraordinary people trying to brighten the lives of patients spending the holidays in hospitals or nursing homes - particularly bringing attention to the wonderful efforts of nurses and hospital staff working hard at transforming clinical environments into warm and friendly places. Celebrity visitors, special meals from the cafeteria, music, and decorations fill the rooms and hospital floors; truly helping patients feel less cut off from family and friends.

Patients receive a great deal of attention (deservedly so), but when addressing the needs of the patient, the loved ones who serve as care- givers can feel relegated to the sidelines. Without diminishing any of the wonderful gestures given to patients, it is important to keep one eye on the caregiver while visiting festively decorated wards. The caregiver's health and well-being serve as the support system for the patient, yet all too often, the needs of the caregiver take a back seat.

Although caregivers often feel reluctant to ask for something for themselves in light of the suffering of their loved one, their own needs are also important. In addition, caregivers also struggle with identifying their needs ...due to the difficulty in defining what "help" looks like in their circumstances. Long-term caregivers seldom allow someone else to carry portions of the load, because experience teaches them, unfortunately, that others often weaken and slip away, leaving them alone to repair the damaged caused by another fractured relationship, and wearily resume the burdens.

During the holiday season, when extra attention is on the chronically ill and disabled, take a moment to look into the corner of the hospital room you visit, and see the one with a weary face and heavy bags under their eyes. If unsure as to what to say, the following questions/conversation starters may be helpful:

- "Are you getting enough sleep?"
- "I have a fabulous recipe that is so easy to reheat and serve...may I bring you a meal?"
- "I'm stopping by the grocery store today, is there something I can pick up for you?"
- "I had to get my oil changed recently...Hey, do you need anything for your car?"
- "Do you need any yard work done, or gutters cleaned? I have a service I use, and it's so easy to get them to swing by and help...my treat."
- "Have you seen your doctor lately?"

Offer to sit with their loved one, so that the caregiver can slip away for their own doctor visit if needed. Since a caregiver probably feels a reluctance to ask for help, the easier you make the decision, the more helpful you will be to them. Caring for caregivers is not complicated; often, they are so tired …that they can sleep anywhere, eat anything , and they gratefully accept kind words when offered.

The eleventh chapter of John speaks to the tenderness of Jesus toward Mary and Martha who cared for their brother, Lazarus, until his death. Acknowledging their grief and pain, Jesus Himself grieved with the distraught sisters.

Now when Mary came to where Jesus was and saw him, she fell at his feet, saying to him, "Lord, if you had been here, my brother would not have died."

When Jesus saw her weeping, and the Jews who had come with her also weeping, he was deeply moved in his spirit and greatly troubled.

And he said, "Where have you laid him?"

They said to him, "Lord, come and see." Jesus wept.

John 11:32-35 English Standard Version

Caregivers know the harsh realities better than most, and do not desire platitudes, but instead require real friends with the courage to shed tears and share grief. When ministering to a caregiver, engage the grief and heartache first …then point to the Savior.

This Christmas and holiday season, make an effort to reach out to a caregiver, and even after the decorations come down. As you do so, it is important to remember that if you love someone, odds are, you will one day be a caregiver yourself ... or receive help from one.

Let each of you look not only to his own interests,
but also to the interests of others.
Philippians 2:4 English Standard Version

Tips from a Case Manager

The following was provided by Gracie's case manager.
An RN, Paul provided HUGE help for Gracie and me during the four
years he served in this role. He and I spoke regularly each month, and
I am grateful for his expertise and friendship.

What is the role of a Case Manager?

According to the Commission for Case Manager
Certification, "The practice of case management is a process
that manages client wellness and autonomy through
advocacy, communication, education and identification and
facilitation of services." Simply put, a case manager will
help a member or their family to better understand their
illness, help educate about that illness as well as to help the
member and family have better control over their lives.

A case manager can provide understanding on how to
access services in a timely, efficient and cost-effective way.
Sometimes a case manager may suggest ways to effectively
manage a service like physical therapy and ways to
maximize a limited benefit to your gain. While doing these
things a case manager is frequently providing emotional
support for those times when the illness may be terminal or
is just overwhelming in its scope and slow recovery.

Some helpful hints: Request a case manager through your

insurance company. Call the customer service number on your (or your loved one's) insurance card, and just simply state that you think you might need a case manager.

Whether dealing with a chronic illness or an acute one, a case man- ager can help you understand and have better control over the recovery. Even if your loved one has a terminal illness, a case manager can assist in accessing and understanding services such as hospice.

If you, or your loved one, require a primary doctor, physical therapist, or even inpatient rehabilitation, a case manager can assist in finding those needed services that are in your network of providers and help you understand how to use your benefits in such a way as to maximize them while being cost-efficient.

Notes

1. Elissa S. Eppel, Dept. of Psychiatry UCSF 12/04

2. Caregiving in the United States, National Alliance for Caregiving in collaboration with AARP; 11/2009

3. MetLife Study of Working Caregivers and Employer Health Costs; National Alliance for Caregiving and MetLife Mature Market Institute. February 2010

4. Care.com and National Family Caregivers Association: State of Care Index. 2009

5. MetLife Caregiving Cost Study: Productivity Losses to U.S.

MetLife Mature Market Institute and National Alliance for Caregiving Business. July 2006.

6. Disability and American Families: 2000, Census 2000 Special Reports, July 2005.

7. National Alliance for Caregiving and Evercare. March 2009

8. Valuing the Invaluable: The Economic Value of Family Caregiving, 2008 Update. AARP

About The Author

As a caregiver for nearly thirty years for his wife, Gracie, Peter often says he has a "PhD in caregiving …from the School of Hard-knocks!"

Peter's caregiving accomplishments are staggering:

- He's managed Gracie's nearly $9,000,000 in health care costs through her seventy-plus operations.
- Although Gracie is considered uninsurable, Peter has changed policies on her 6 times - without even an hour's gap in coverage.
- He has worked with more than sixty physicians.
- Cared for Gracie in 12 different hospitals (6 of them inpatient).
- Never lost an insurance appeal.

Peter often laughs when stating that he's waiting for the phone call from Washington to invite him to help address America's health care *issues!*

From *Fox News* to the *Today* show, and *People* to *Web MD*, Peter and his family have a lengthy list of media credits sharing their amazing story—and Peter has an extensive media, speaking, and writing history where he discusses disability and family/marriage issues, caregiving, and other related topics. In addition to a lengthy list of published articles, Peter served as the writer for Gracie's book, *Gracie-Standing With Hope* (2010 Liberty University Press).

Weaving his outrageous (and contagious) humor into the painful issues of chronic illness, caregiving, and suffering, Peter's kept audiences laughing across the country. When people understand that it's OK to laugh a little, even while struggling, it makes the journey just a little easier. Taking his deep understanding of caregiving and his outrageous sense of humor to the airwaves, Peter launched a radio talk show to caregivers. *Facebook.com/thepeterrosenbergershow*

Peter also serves as the president of *Standing With Hope* the non-profit prosthetic limb outreach he and Gracie founded. Collecting used prosthetic limbs from around the country, they work with Corrections Corporation of America through a unique inmate work program—where inmates disassemble the used limbs in order to recycle useable parts. Those parts, and other purchased materials, are sent to workers in Ghana, West Africa, where *Standing With Hope* provides ongoing training to equip local workers to build limbs for their own people.

Peter and Gracie live in Nashville, Tennessee with their dog, Mack. Their oldest son, Parker and his wife, Viveka, live in Birmingham. Their youngest son, Grayson, lives in Nashville and is in the entertainment business.

For More Information Visit
www.caregiverswithhope.com
www.standingwithhope.com
Facebook.com/standingwithhope
@standwithhope

Made in the USA
Lexington, KY
02 October 2015